WINE GROWING
IN ENGLAND

THE COUNTRYMAN LIBRARY

Others in preparation

THE COUNTRYMAN LIBRARY

WINE GROWING IN ENGLAND

BY

George Ordish

Go thy way, eat thy bread with joy and
drink thy wine with a merry heart.
Ecclesiastes ix. 7

RUPERT HART-DAVIS
36 Soho Square, London W.1
1953

PRINTED IN GREAT BRITAIN BY
WESTERN PRINTING SERVICES LTD. BRISTOL

To Hugh Blunt

CONTENTS

ILLUSTRATIONS

9

PREFACE

WHEN I was young I used to work as an entomologist in France. I was much struck by the fact that the small farmer always made his own wine, quite easily; and that many vineyards were covered with snow in the winter. When I came to live in Kent I found the climate not unlike the Champagne, and when in Sir Henry Ellis's work on the Domesday Book I found we had had at least thirty-eight vineyards at the Conquest I immediately planted some vines.

Some good wine and this book are the results. They embody my experience of fifteen years of wine-making.

I am greatly indebted to many friends for their help, particularly to Major Blunt and Mr. Fussell for bibliographical notes, and to Mr. Rollo Hardman, secretary of the Wine Trade Club, for permission to use their library. I am indebted to Messrs. Plant Protection Ltd. for much assistance and some photographs and finally I would like to thank my wife for many helpful suggestions with the manuscript.

GEORGE ORDISH

Yalding
April 1953

Chapter One

INTRODUCTION

IT is not as difficult as one might think to grow grapes and make wine in England, and it is an immensely interesting and satisfying occupation. Typical autumn weather in Britain consists of hot days and cold still nights, and it is at this time of year that the wine-maker is busy. From his fermenting vats or tubs comes a tiny unforgettable and thrilling sound. The noise is unique and almost indescribable, but it is like the whispering of a thousand tiny leaves or the crinkling of ghostly tissue paper; it is the crushed grapes fermenting, and the sound is made by the bursting, on the surface, of countless little bubbles of carbon dioxide gas. At the same time a pleasant, fresh smell fills the outhouse or fermenting room. The sound and smell of the "must" starting to work are things that the amateur wine-maker will always remember.

There is a curious difference between Britain and most of the nations in Europe with regard to their attitude towards wine. In the former it is regarded as something of a luxury, to be used only on special occasions, and in the latter as a necessity. In most of Europe during the war wine was rationed in much the same way as foods such as butter and meat. When, recently, I was arranging for my daughter to stay with a French family, Madame Dupont told me she did not allow her children to drink much tea or coffee as it was too exciting for the nerves; they had wine instead! It was, of course, usually diluted with a little water, and this strikingly demonstrates our difference of attitude. There is no lack of appreciation of wine here, as

may be seen by the fact that much of the finest of French
wine is reserved for Britain, and its lack of everyday accept-
ance seems to me to be due to a long chain of circumstances.
In the first place, in the eighteenth century, the enmity of
England and France led Pitt to tax the heavy Portuguese
wines at a much lower rate than the French, which encouraged the drinking of port. This is not a table wine
one can drink every day and consequently the custom
began to fade. At this time the distillers were producing
large quantities of cheap gin, with somewhat unwelcome
social effects, as Hogarth's print "Gin Lane" emphasizes.
To counteract these, the tax on gin was gradually raised
and, having lost the habit of drinking light table wines, the
population turned to beer. The fine hops and barley found
in England produced excellent beer and everyday wine-
drinking continued to decline. In recent years the excise
duties on wine have been increased considerably; before the
war they were 8d. per bottle and today they are 1s. 9d.;
nevertheless in terms of alcohol content the duty per unit
of alcohol is about the same for beer and wine, whereas for
spirits it is some seven times higher.

At the same time a kind of mystique has grown up
around the subject of wine, which cult is greatly encouraged
by wine waiters in fashionable restaurants. The mystique
is to the effect that the whole subject is extremely difficult,
that only years of experience can make one a connoisseur
and that, in choosing a wine, one can make frightful mis-
takes and expose oneself to the derision of all spectators.
I am the last to deny that there are many fine old wines
which can only be fully appreciated by knowledge and
experience of the subject, but I cannot help feeling this
attitude is overdone and that it may deter many people
from using this pleasant, generous and healthy product.
With wines one should be more like that famous visitor to

the art gallery who declared that, though she did not know anything about art, yet she knew what she liked. Liking a wine seems to me to be a good and sufficient reason for drinking it, whether it bears a famous name or not (though it may be a poor basis for the study of the arts).

There are a great many reasons for drinking wine: to keep warm, to keep cool, to aid digestion, to stimulate the saliva, to disinfect the water, for one's health, for friendship and so forth, but the fact that one likes it seems to me to be the best and soundest reason for doing so. It is surprising what a difference a glass of wine will make to a meal; it can be the making of a dinner party and even with bread and cheese it can turn a "snack" into a meal. To drink wine every day, however, is expensive, but to make and drink one's own wine is not, and moreover the making of it is not difficult and is in itself a source of immense satisfaction.

There are very many different kinds of wine whose characteristics and flavours depend on variety, climate, situation and season. English wines can stand on their own merits and the grower should not try to imitate foreign wines, but should aim at a good sound wine with its own attributes: this was the advice of Phillip Miller, the famous gardener, introducer of plants and author of the *Gardener's Dictionary* (1739). The English grower will find that reds made from Brandt resemble clarets in general type, and whites from the same grape are like still champagne.

Let us examine a bottle of 1945 Kentish Brandt, a very good season. It must be taken from the rack in a cradle and the cork carefully pulled because there is quite a lot of deposit. Though generally this is firmly stuck to the bottle, we do not want to take any risk of disturbing it. Poured into a clear glass it will be seen to be beautifully transparent, a deep red with no trace of purple in it and thus slightly different in colour from a Bordeaux. The scent (or "bouquet") of the wine is fresh and fragrant but not too strong. The flavour on the tongue and palate is good, and the tannin seems to be high enough to balance the acidity, in spite of the amount deposited on the glass. The after taste or quality of softness ("velouté") is there and we can decide that this is a wine to drink with beef and cheese dishes, and that we could do with a lot more of it in the cellar!

Wine grapes grow well in the open in England provided the right varieties and situations are chosen. The idea is not a new one, as old records show that most of the monasteries in the southern half of England had a vineyard attached and many vineyards along the Medway valley are mentioned in the Domesday Book. The last open-air plantation of any size in Britain was that of the Marquis of Bute in Glamorgan; it was planted in 1875, described in *Country Life* in 1904, produced a vast quantity of good wine, some of which sold at auction for as much as 115s. per dozen, and finally disappeared during the 1914 war.

Today the subject is being revived and there are many houses and gardens growing grapes in the open for wine, and even a few small plantations. I myself have been making wine for fifteen years and have three sides of my house and various trellises in the garden producing wine grapes for this purpose. Whilst we cannot expect to rival the "grands crus" of Bordeaux and Burgundy, we can readily produce very pleasant drinkable wines, and we may even make very good ones from time to time, as the price quoted above for the Marquis of Bute's Glamorgan vintage shows. Nine shillings and ninepence per bottle fifty years ago, when wine could be freely imported, is a guarantee of quality.

Many fruits produce a smaller but better-flavoured crop when they are growing on the edge of their climatic range;

examples are seen in apples, which are better in England than in France; peaches which are better in France than in Spain, and oranges which are better in Spain than in North Africa. The same effect may well be produced with the vine, whose northern limit, with our present varieties, appears to be the climate associated with the 53 degrees parallel in England, though new varieties may well extend this range northward.

The 53rd parallel runs from the Wash to Caernarvon Bay and passes just north of Boston and just south o Stoke-on-Trent, and personally I feel the vine will thrive well to the north of this line provided the sites are well chosen and early varieties are used: for instance, there is already a thriving vine nursery at Formby, Lancashire, and a Dr. Goddard in the seventeenth century thought the vine would grow in Scotland because of the long summer days there.

Some consideration must be given to "photoperiodism", a recent discovery of the botanists. This is the response of plants to the length of day. Some plants such as chrysanthemums and some potatoes require a short day in order to produce flowers and this they do not get in northern latitudes. The long day seems to prevent flowering and chrysanthemums thus tend to flower in the autumn, as the day shortens. Certain modern varieties do, however, flower in our long-day summer. The land of origin of the vine appears to be Asia Minor and one would expect it to be a moderately short-day plant, but the fact that a plant originated in a certain climate does not mean that it will not thrive, or even do better, in another, and not all plants do badly when grown in climates where the length of day differs from that of their native homes. In fact amongst plants much setback due to a different "light periodicity" may be said to be the exception rather than the rule.

B

In order to thrive the vine needs: (i) a dormant period, (ii) freedom from late spring frosts, (iii) sufficient light to grow during the summer, and (iv) sufficient autumn sun and heat to raise the sugar content and reduce the acid level in the fruit to an acceptable standard.

The dormant period is obtained anywhere with a temperate zone climate. Freedom from spring frosts is usually a question of site and this may well be an important limiting factor, as is also the question of summer light and heat. I here put a question to which I do not yet know the answer—will the much longer day in say Scotland with its lower, but longer, intensity of light make up for the stronger, but shorter duration, light in the south? I think that with certain varieties of grapes it very probably will. The next point is the autumn ripening and our new short-season grapes may well get sufficient autumn heat to ripen; moreover, artificial ripening of picked grapes in a warm room may not be impossible. I would not hold it impossible to grow good wine grapes on a house or garden wall in Scotland. Dessert grapes grow in greenhouses in that country, so presumably the long day is not an adverse factor.

The Excise Tax on light still wines, that is those containing less than 15 per cent by volume of alcohol (equal to 27 degrees of "proof spirit"), is 10s. 6d. per gallon, but the home wine-maker does not have to pay this duty provided he does not sell his wine. He can make, consume and give away as much as he likes! Thus, apart from the interest of the pursuit of wine-making, the amateur starts with a cash advantage of 1s. 9d. per bottle.

This book is written from my own experience and describes nothing that I have not done myself (except where noted), and all measures recommended are those which have shown themselves to be successful, at any rate, under my conditions, and likely to be so elsewhere.

I propose to give some historical notes, to describe the methods of planting and growing grapes and the control of diseases and insects; then I shall describe what wine is and the principles of fermentation, before I deal with making wine, red, white, and sparkling, and country wines; that is wines made not from grapes, but from other fruits or flowers, such as plum or cowslip. Finally I shall describe the apparatus needed, and consider the possibilities of commercial production in Britain.

Chapter Two

THE HISTORY OF GRAPES AND WINE
IN ENGLAND

It has been suggested that the Romans brought the vine
plant to England, and though there is but little documen-
tary evidence of this, it is a fact that the Emperor Domitian
(A.D. 81–96) passed an edict prohibiting the growing of the
vine in Britain, presumably in the interests of the home
country's trade, and that subsequently Probus repealed the
edict about A.D. 280 and allowed the culture of the grape
here.

The early church took an interest in the vine and the
Venerable Bede (died 735) mentions that vines are found
in a few places. The laws of Alfred (871–901) and of
Edgar (957–975) refer to vineyards and the Domesday Book
mentions no fewer than thirty-eight, most of them being
attached to monasteries. They were so numerous at Ely
that the district was known as the "Isle of Vines".

These were undoubtedly vineyards; it has been main-
tained that the early records, written in Latin, meant an
orchard by the word "vinea", but this is not so as both
vines and apples are frequently referred to in the same
sentence. It must be remembered, though, that the wine
drunk in Britain during Norman times and in the Middle
Ages was very different from that of today. Our ancestors
liked it raw and strong. They seem to have drunk it very
soon after fermentation, whilst wine of more than a year
old was considered of very bad quality and fetched a lower
price; and, of course, it may well have been poor in many
cases, as old wine would in all probability have been

attacked by vinegar bacteria or by the *Mycoderma* fungus both of which would have ruined it. It is unlikely in those days that they knew much about bottling wine, or the nature of ferments; in fact it is for less than a hundred years that we have known anything about the fundamentals of fermentation ourselves. Consequently, the wine, probably around 8 per cent in alcohol, had to be drunk young or it would "turn" and become unserviceable.

Throughout our history constant references to vineyards and wine-making can be found, and I summarize the main citations in the bibliography which gives the date and type of event recorded or books published, and the primary and secondary references. I regret that I have not been able to check personally all the primary references, as many of them are in very obscure or difficult books and documents, but I have not included any which I think are at all doubtful.

From this table we can see that there have always been a few vineyards and wine-makers in England, and we must ask ourselves why it never established itself as a major industry, as did brewing and cider-making. The short answer is that beer and cider were easier to make and more profitable; when we examine the matter in more detail several interesting facts emerge. In Roman times wine-growers in Britain must have been very inexperienced and were no doubt trying to use Italian varieties and methods; it must have been only slowly that varieties suited to our soil and climate were selected out. Only the upper classes drank wine. The early English kings seem to have taken to it and apparently most monasteries had a vineyard, but all this production was for home consumption; there was no trade in the home-produced liquor. The accession of Bordeaux to the English crown in 1152 made the Garonne part of the king's dominions and meant that the fine claret wines were freely available. Wine is easily shipped, and the government of those days encouraged the trade because it facilitated collection of taxes and stimulated the building of sea-going vessels. There were, moreover, more profitable crops than grapes in England, such as wheat, barley and wool.

We still did not have really suitable varieties, and so vines during the sixteenth and seventeenth centuries were only found on a small scale. Towards the end of the seventeenth century we find an author (John Beale, 1677) recommending the addition of sugar to the must, and an interesting development is the realization that the strength of the wine is dependent on the amount of sugar present, and that tests can be made for this substance. In the *Closet of the Eminently Learned Sir Kenelm Digby* we find the author recommending what is in effect a hydrometer; that is, to add honey until "a fresh egg floats to the depth of twopence". This method might still be used today with advantage, provided we could find such an article. A not so fresh egg will float higher than a fresh one, and introduce errors. Honey was a comparatively expensive commodity then, but it must have considerably improved the wine in bad seasons and have helped weak musts from unsuitable grapes at all times. There were both good and bad wines made at this time. John Evelyn, in 1655, writes ". . . to see Colonel Blount's subterranean warren and drunk of the wine of his vineyard, which was good for little". Colonel Blount was a great friend of Sir Thomas Hanmer, who was an enthusiastic owner of and writer about vineyards. In 1665 John Rose describes good wines made from his vines, and he offers plants to all inquirers. A Dr. Goddard at this time thought vines would thrive even in Scotland, on account of the longer summer day there, which may well be true today.

The biggest successful vineyard of the eighteenth century

was that of the Hon. Chas. Hamilton, at Pain's Hill, Surrey, which is today a block of flats. The making of the wine there is described in some detail by Sir Edward Barry in his book *Observations, Historical, Critical and Medical on the Wines of the Ancients, and the Analogy between them and the Modern Wines* (T. Cadell, London, 1775).

The planting of vines and fruit must have been discouraged by the granting of a letters patent to Peter Le Brocq, about 1786, for an elaborate method of growing devised by him. Le Brocq threatened to prosecute all who used his system without payment of a fee, and though it was too involved to be of any use yet it seems that people hesitated to plant up through uncertainty as to what exactly Le Brocq's method was. A Monsieur Vispré, however, defied him in his book on vines in England, published in 1786 in London, and in another published in 1787, also in London, but in French, he discusses the possibilities of wine-growing in Britain, which he thinks would be good were it not for Le Brocq's patent.

Sugar was now coming in from the West Indies on a bigger scale, and wine-makers started using it, but in such big amounts that they spoiled a promising industry. Instead of trying to establish English wines on their own merits the would-be vintners started to imitate foreign vintages, or made their wines very strong, adding many colouring and flavouring substances. A book such as the *Innkeeper's and Butler's Guide, or a Directory of British Wines* (J. Davies, 6th edition, 1808), gives recipes and directions for making dozens of what must have been very nauseous imitations. This seems to have been the general attitude during the nineteenth century, with one notable exception—the Marquis of Bute.

In the past there must have been many vineyards, because even today (1953), particularly in the West Country, traces of them can still be seen in the terraced hillsides. A particularly interesting one is at Claverton, Somerset. In Savage and Meylor's map, 1802, of "Bath and 5 miles around" a vineyard is clearly shown near this village. When I looked at the modern Ordnance Survey map the same spot was called "Vineyard Farm", and it was with great interest that I went out to see this place in its (from the map) obviously steep valley. The terraced vineyard on the hillside, though grass-grown, could still clearly be seen, and the owners, Mrs. Godwin and her sons, told me that there were a few vines growing there when they took the place over in 1936. It was an ideal spot, a bow facing south with the grassed terraces, about 2 ft. wide and 300 yds. long, covering about three acres of ground. In the barn traces of the press could still be found, particularly the huge oak bearer with a hand-cut wooden thread, which carried the press tree of about a foot in diameter. This could, of course, have been a cider press, but the terraces, the name, and the old vines lead me to think it must at least have pressed grapes as well.

The last commercial vineyards in Britain were those of the Marquis of Bute at Castle Coch and Swanbridge. Mr. Andrew Pettigrew started the planting in 1875 with the variety "Gamay noir", and large and high-grade crops were obtained. In 1881, the year of the great snowstorm, a very big and good crop was picked. The wine was all sold to a merchant at 5s. per bottle. Some of this, auctioned a year later, fetched 9s. 7d. per bottle, which is a good enough certificate of its quality. This excellent vineyard seems to have disappeared during the 1914 World War.

Today there are several enthusiasts growing their own grapes and making wine, but no one is doing it, as far as I am aware, on a big scale. I planted my own vines in 1938; Mr. Hyams has established a fine vineyard near Canterbury, and Mr. Barrington Brock is carrying out a series of most interesting experiments in Surrey. Mrs. Tritton and Mr. Pollard are pioneers in the West. There are at least ten successful outdoor vines in London, and no doubt many others elsewhere.

The vine came to England and flourished; it was grown by the Church and by kings and noble families, but it was a difficult crop and needed skilled attention. It did not flourish as an industry because other crops gave better returns: this was because of lack of knowledge and just that difference of climate that made good sites rarer in Britain than in France. It was cheaper to obtain wine by trading wheat or wool for it than by growing it. This trading, moreover, encouraged the building of ships and also gave the government an easily taxable article. In the nineteenth century, with the very notable exception of Castle Coch, cheap sugar encouraged the production of poor imitations of too strong a nature which never allowed an industry to start.

Today, however, we have knowledge and better varieties for our climate, so that there is no reason why the Castle Coch experiment should not be repeated. An industry could be established, though there are numerous difficulties, not the least being the Customs and Excise regulations. There is no reason, however, why most householders should not grow and make their own wines, which is an interesting pastime and an inexpensive method of obtaining a health-giving drink.

Chapter Three

GROWING THE GRAPES

THE vine appears to have originated in the Caucasus region many thousands of years ago as a remarkably hardy woodland creeper known to us as *Vitis vinifera* sp. *silvestris* Gmel. This plant is now extinct and is found only as fossil remains. It seems to have been very vigorous and long-lived, and it spread over and was supported by the forest trees. From this ancestor the European species of vine arose, known as *Vitis vinifera* spp. *sativa* D.C., which is now represented by many hundreds of different varieties. Botanically, *Vitis* belongs to the family of *Vitaceae*, which includes among others the genera of *Cissus* and *Ampelopsis* climbers, which last is the well-known Virginia creeper. The reader interested in the origin and spread of the vine should read Viala's and Hyams' books.

Although *V. vinifera* gives the best wine, there are other species which can be used for this purpose, of which two are the American *V. lubrusca* and *V. riparia*. The former is known as the fox grape, and a certain amount of wine is made from it in the United States and Mexico. This wine seems very strongly flavoured to a European palate, but in Mexico it is becoming increasingly popular as a drink, perhaps because it contrasts very favourably, at any rate to my palate, with the aloe products *pulque* and *tequila*. Other species of the *Vitacea* produce edible fruits, though they do not appear to be cultivated; the value of such plants and the other *Vitis* species is more in their potential use as breeding material for producing new useful varieties than as actual crops in themselves. Mention must also be made of a species

V. vinifera purpurea, which has a highly coloured purple, though rather acid, fruit. It is grown as a decorative plant in England, but is also useful for the purpose of adding colour to wine, and acidity also if this is needed.

There is a popular belief that the vine can only thrive in the open in a very hot climate and that frost is fatal to it. This is by no means the case. The vine is a temperate zone plant; its range has been given as from 33° North to 53° North, but there is no doubt that in sheltered positions it can thrive both north and south of this belt: in the case of the northern extension the shelter must be arranged to catch the sun, and in the southern one to give shelter from it. The climatic range of the vine is being extended both north and south by the breeding of new varieties, which will support cooler conditions and a longer summer day for the north, and the opposite state for the south. During the dormant period the vine is remarkably tolerant of cold weather. The vineyards of the Champagne are frequently covered with snow and those of Canada and parts of the United States and Russia are regularly inundated with it every year. The vines are protected by ploughing soil over the stock. One of the limiting factors in the spread of the vine southwards is that the winter weather is not severe enough to check growth in the vine, and to give the necessary winter pause without which fruiting will not take place. The main climatic need of the vine is a warm, dry autumn, and any climate that will ripen apples well will also ripen some varieties of grapes. Another encouraging factor for the English wine grower is the fact that many fruits seem to produce the best quality when on the climatic edge of cultivation. For instance, the best coffee is grown at high altitudes.

A hundred years ago all vines in Europe were grown on their own roots and propagated by cuttings or layers. This is still the case in the main in England, but not so on the Continent. The reason is the existence there of the insect known as the *Phylloxera*. The story of the *Phylloxera* is fairly well known, but I will summarize it here. The *Phylloxera* is an American aphid which lives on the leaves of the American vines, where it forms small galls and does no particular harm. In about 1870 it found its way to Europe and started to attack the European vine (*V. vinifera*). On this vine it was able to live both on the leaves and the roots, and this last facility was disastrous as the roots were killed and the plant died. In France, thousands of acres of vines began to die, until the work of Ripley, a young American entomologist, and of Foëx indicated that the solution was to graft the European grape with its good qualities of fruit on to the American rootstock which was resistant to the insect. Today in Europe nearly all vineyards are grafted on to resistant rootstocks, but Britain is clear of this pest; consequently, most vines in Britain grow on their own roots. Great care must be taken by anyone bringing vines into Britain not to introduce this terrible insect with them.

Suitable Varieties. There are a number of varieties of wine grape which do well in the open in England. Many old houses in Kent, Surrey, Hampshire and even London have vines growing on them to which it is difficult to assign a name. Up to a few years ago it was generally accepted that the most suitable varieties to grow were either a cutting of one of these old vines which were obviously doing well in the neighbourhood, or Black Hamburgh (also famous as a hothouse grape at Hampton Court), Black Cluster, Brandt (a black grape) or Royal Muscadine (a white); but recently Gamay Hatif des Vosges (black), Madeleine Royale (white) and S.9110 (white) have shown great possibilities. The vine nurseries at Formby, Lancs, offer all the above varieties and some seventeen more as well, which include six new French hybrids, all recommended for use in England.

I myself only have experience here of Brandt, Black Cluster, Royal Muscadine (or Chasselas doré), Madeleine Royale and Gamay. I find Brandt by far the best for my conditions, closely followed by Gamay Hatif. Brandt is a hybrid of a Canadian and a European grape; it is extremely vigorous, a deep rooter and a free bearer. It makes a good red wine very like a Bordeaux claret, or it can be used to make a dry white wine reminiscent of still champagne. There is, however, a certain amount of confusion over the names of grape varieties, and I think there are at least two strains of Brandt.

I find Black Hamburgh of little use out of doors and Black Cluster makes very weak growth. The Formby vine nurseries add the variety Meslier Précoce, a very early white with small berries, to the list of successful outdoor wine varieties but I have not tried it myself.

Many experiments are being made with seedlings and hybrids, and no doubt in a few years time we shall possess varieties suitable for a much wider range of climates, with opportunities of yet better vintages. The grower's choice would thus seem to be among the following at present:

(i) *Blacks*. Brandt, Gamay Hatif des Vosges.

(ii) *Whites*. Madeleine Royale, Meslier Précoce and S.9110.

Grapes will grow on almost any soil, and they have an advantage that in general the poorer the soil the better is the wine, though of course the quantity of fruit produced per unit of area is less. The highest quality in wine is usually obtained from grapes grown on a thin limestone soil, so that when planting a vine it is advisable to add a little lime or old broken mortar.

Site. Vines may be grown either against a wall or in open ground. In the first position they will thrive further north than in the second.

The best exposure for a wall grape is southerly, either due south or south-east or south-west. A south-facing wall has the advantage over open planting that the reflected heat in the autumn will ripen the grapes well and raise the sugar content. A northern aspect is not, of course, any use, and they will not be really worth while growing on a wall facing north-east or north-west. One can plan to cover the whole wall with a single plant, or to plant vines at regular intervals. which may be as low as a yard, when each vine is grown as a cordon, or any other convenient distance may be used. In the first system one needs only one plant, which is cheaper, but it is slower in getting the whole wall covered, and also an accident to or a disease in the one vine root will destroy the whole vine, whereas with several plants only a proportion is lost.

For vines in the open any site suitable for dessert apples will do. The main requirement is that it should be free from late spring frosts. The ideal position is one with a southerly slope, as this will concentrate the summer and autumn heat of the sun. The famous vineyard of the Marquis of Bute at Castle Coch had a south-eastern exposure.

Planting. The planting should be done in the autumn or winter, and the procedure is much the same as in planting a rose or fruit tree. A hole is dug about a foot from the wall, a little lime and compost worked into the bottom, the roots are spread out and the earth is filled in. A little more compost is spread over the surface to keep the roots warm during the winter and the vine is cut right back to leave three strong buds.

Training Wall Vines. In the year of planting the vine will grow and may even throw a flower shoot which should be removed, as the first season must be devoted to the production of the wood. The shoots may be trained over the wall in any way that suits the area to be covered or the fancy of the grower. In general, it is better to keep the shoots (or rods) at least gently rising, and a dip is to be avoided, though it may be necessary at times in order to get round a window. Some arrangement must be made to hold the vine to the wall. Nails and pieces of cloth can be used, but they have to be renewed as the rods swell and the cloth rots. The most satisfactory method is to strain wire parallel to the ground over the surface of the wall; there is then always something to which the vine can be tied both in summer and winter, and the wall is less damaged by permanent wirework than by constantly knocking in nails. 10 or 12 gauge galvanized wire is used; the first wire should be at 18 inches from the ground and the remainder at intervals of 2 ft. or 2 ft. 6 in. up to the top of the wall, or the gutters if a house is being wired. Each wire is fastened to a base peg, which must be firmly fastened into the mortar, or preferably into the brick itself, and threaded through galvanized eyelets which are driven into the mortar at about six-foot intervals. The wire is led finally to an anchor peg. The wire must be strained tight against the peg. This can be done by getting it as tight as possible by pulling on it and then incorporating a threaded wire strainer in each wire; or one can tighten the wire quite satisfactorily by using pulley blocks and rope. One light 3-pulley block and one 2-pulley one and a thin rope or strong cord will strain the wire adequately, provided something solid can be found to which the 2-pulley block can be temporarily anchored. The procedure is as follows: After the wire has been threaded through the eyelets in the wall it is cut well past the anchor peg and a loop made in it; the hook of the 3-pulley block already threaded with the rope is put in the loop and the rope is pulled. The wire is strained over the anchor peg and when it is tight enough the wire is tapped with a hammer to bend it a little round the peg; at the same time the pulley is slackened a little. If the wire is now held against the peg the pulley hook can be taken out and the wire twisted round the anchor peg to make it secure. This system saves the cost of strainers, but it does mean that it is difficult subsequently to take up any slack that may arise. If a house is more or less rectangular a wire may be threaded through eyelets right round the building and tightened against itself with a screw-threaded wire strainer fastened to the two ends of the wire. In this case blocks of smooth wood in the shape of an L must be fitted to the corners and a groove cut in them. These are fitted under the wire, which can thus slip as it is tightened. The wire on the north side will not be wanted, but this system does mean that the two firm anchor pegs, which need care in fixing, are not required. This system can only be used above the level of door tops, and in the case of a house some wires may pass in front of windows, and here again it cannot be employed if the windows are cottage casements, as it would stop them being opened. The wire can also be strained around three sides of a house provided blocks of smooth wood are used at the corners, which will allow the wire to slip as the strainer is tightened; this means that two anchor pegs must be provided. The vine rods and shoots are tied to the wires with coconut string (hop string) or well-covered electric wire, and the rods are trained outside the wire. It is less work to have them inside the wire, as they are more or less self-supporting then, but here the rods will eventually become too thick and will suffer from restriction by being squeezed between the wire and the wall. A vigorous vine will easily have reached the eaves of a two-storey house in five years from planting.

Three great advantages of wall-trained vines are: (i) in

(*Opposite*) Part of an illuminated 11th-century MS. of the book of Genesis in Latin and Saxon. It shows a vineyard with the vines supported on posts, and the grapes being pressed. (*By kind permission of the British Museum.*)

(*Above*) A red vine in Bloomsbury taken on December 20th, showing all leaf gone bu fruit still sound. (*Below*) "Vineyard Farm", Claverton, Somerset. The terraces which must have held vines, are clearly seen through the grass.

a garden they do not take up space required for flowers or vegetables, (ii) the wall gives protection against late spring frosts, and (iii) the heat reflected by the wall gives good quality and a high sugar content to the grapes.

Planting in the Open. In open ground vines may be planted much as they are in France, or they may be grown on high trellis work. They may be on a short leg with no support, or each one may be grown on a stake, but the most satisfactory method is to grow them on trellis wiring either low or high.

Low trellising is the system most employed in France. The vines are planted along wirework much as soft fruit is planted in England. The top wire is about 3 ft. high supported on stakes at 10 ft. intervals. Beneath the top wire one or two more wires are provided. The wires are led through stout end posts which are suitably supported and are strained tight either with pulley blocks, or by means of threaded strainers. The rows should be about the same distance apart from each other as they are high above the ground, and the vines should be planted at about one yard intervals in the row. In this system the vines are not allowed to make any permanent branches or "rods" as they are called, but the shoots are pruned back each year to the short leg which gradually grows stouter and stouter.

This system uses a lot of plants, in fact 4,840 per acre, but gives quick returns, and allows changes of varieties or replacement of failing plants to be made rapidly. There is an advantage in England in keeping the bottom wire low (about 1 ft. above the ground) as in a dry autumn (and most of our autumns are dry) the heat reflected from the soil will ripen the grapes well; but it also has the disadvantage that some of the grapes will rest on the soil and will start rotting in wet weather. In a garden this system of a low trellis may well be used as a background to a flower

C

bed; the vine will, of course, project shoots forward and consequently flowers planted within 1 ft. or 18 in. of it will not thrive. The roots of the vine tend to go deep and will take very little nourishment from the bed. The Brandt variety is very decorative and has attractively coloured foliage in the autumn.

High Trellis Planting. In the high trellis system the methods used are much the same as on a wall, which last is replaced by a system of wires and posts. The vine grows each year from its permanent rods which are tied to the wires. Such a trellis makes a good screen between a flower and vegetable garden. On a production or commercial scale the low wiring is more advantageous than the high.

Six to eight feet high is the best for high trellis work. The bottom wire should be at 18 in. from the ground and the remaining wires at approximately 2 ft. intervals from this. The wires are supported by posts at 10 ft. intervals, and a vine may be planted a little distance from each post, but here again it is possible to vary the distance and the vines can be grown as single-stem cordons at 3 ft. intervals, or with long rods at 30 or 40 ft. spacing. The supports for the wires must be sunk in the soil 3 or 4 ft. and may be of wood or iron. Chestnut or ash posts are suitable, but oak will be longer lasting, and they must be treated with a preservative before being set in the ground; posts can sometimes be purchased already treated, or they can be doctored at home. Painting with a wood preservative is good, but hot soaking is better. Tanks for this method are a common sight in any country-side growing hops, but the same methods can be improvised at home. A dustbin or open-topped drum is arranged over some bricks so that a small fire can be lit under it. The posts are put into the bin and the preservative poured in; tar oil or gas tar is very suitable (a highly inflammable product is not desirable for this method). The fire is lit and when all is well heated it is extinguished and the whole left at least twenty-four hours to cool. The advantage of this system is that the heat expands air in the tissue of the wood which escapes, and as the solution cools the wood draws in the preservative in its place. The posts should be allowed to drain before being set out and the wire holes drilled; a dab of preservative over each hole will not come amiss.

A solution of copper sulphate can be used to preserve wooden posts, and a copper copper, which is rare these days, makes an ideal vessel in which to carry out the process, as it can be heated. Containers made from other metals, such as zinc or iron, cannot be used with this salt. If a wooden barrel is used to hold the posts and copper sulphate solution, it must on no account be used subsequently for any wine-making operation, as traces of the salt in the barrel would have disastrous effects on the wine.

Galvanized iron pipes of 2 in. diameter or more make excellent supports for wirework. 12 ft. lengths should be drilled with four $\frac{1}{8}$ in. holes right through to take the wires, starting at 2 in. from the top and at 2 ft. intervals. The top and bottom of the pipe are brushed with bituminous paint, as are also the drilled holes, in order to stop rusting. Iron pipe or angle iron can also be used, but must be well painted with bitumen. The end posts must be very firmly anchored, which may be done by bracing them with a support inside the wire or by an anchor outside. When the posts have been set out 10 ft. apart and with $4\frac{1}{2}$ ft. in the soil and anchored, the wires are threaded through, secured at one end, and tightened with threaded wire strainers on each wire, rather than with pulleys, as frequent adjustment may be needed.

It is convenient to train the vine up the post to get the rods for each wire, but the preservative on wooden posts is toxic to vine roots, so that in the case of newly treated posts it is as well to plant the young vines about 18 in. from the post and train the shoot towards it.

Training and Pruning. The object of training and pruning is to produce wood from which fruiting shoots will grow each year. The soft green shoots which spring from buds harden during the summer and autumn and form buds in the axils of the leaves from which shoots will spring. The flowers are produced from a node opposite a leaf and consequently the aim is to produce strong healthy buds which will be able to throw shoots capable of pushing out flowers. The vine, however, is not pruned with the same object in mind as is the apple, where the aim is to get fewer but larger fruits. In the case of vines for wine-making we wish to get as much total weight of ripe fruit as possible, and the actual size of the berries or of the bunch is not of much importance. Consequently, an unpruned vine would produce as much, or even more fruit than a pruned one, but it would very rapidly deteriorate and leave a lot of dying and dead wood which would in subsequent years produce only poor crops. Even in its heydey the unpruned plant would not ripen its fruit well; consequently, the object of pruning the vine is to ensure continuity of production and ripening of the fruit.

Winter pruning must be done at that season and not in the spring, nor when there is the slightest movement of sap. The vine is a plant which does not form a callus when cut, consequently it will "bleed" very badly if pruned after the beginning of February. This is a most important point. It is extremely difficult to stop the bleeding of a vine, and it will lose pints of fluid from a single late cut and greatly weaken itself. Winter pruning allows the cells immediately below the cut to wither and dry up, and thus safely seals the shoot against loss of sap.

This bleeding will not occur when the green summer shoots are pruned.

Greenhouse grapes are usually thinned in the early summer with the same object as apple thinning, to produce bigger fruit, but this is not necessary with outdoor vines for wine as no extra weight or ripeness of fruit is secured by thinning and it is an immense labour.

I will now deal with training and pruning in two parts, the first on walls and high trellis and the second on vines in open ground on stakes or low trellis work.

1. *Walls and High Trellis.* In the summer after planting the vine will make at least two good shoots; these may be trained out either to make a T with the stem, or to form the basis of a fan-training system. The latter is easier to manage, but the former is neater and more striking. In the following winter the two arms of the T are pruned back about one-third to a strong bud, and the same treatment is given to the rods of the fan-trained vine. Some vines may take time to get established and only make a few inches of growth the first season, and others may shoot out six feet or more. Any flowers that are formed in the first season must be removed as we must concentrate on production of wood.

In the second summer a number of shoots will be produced, and these are tied in for the purpose of continuing the framework. From the horizontal top arms of the T shoots are taken up vertically and two more continue the horizontal arms of the T. The fan shape of the other system is carried on by securing other shoots at appropriate places. During this season some fruit will be formed and the shoots carrying fruit must be "stopped" by picking off the end of the shoot a few leaves above the bunch. In the winter the vine is pruned and the shoots needed to continue the framework are cut back to sound wood; the others are cut back to form spurs, usually to two strong buds, but some varieties may need more buds, up to six.

The prunings may be used for propagating more vines;

they root readily, particularly if soaked in "Hortomone A" beforehand.

The shoots are cut into lengths having three or four buds each, soaked overnight in the hormone solution and planted out in light soil the next day.

In this way the vine is extended and spur pruned year by year until the whole wall is covered; when this stage is reached only spur pruning is used. After ten or fifteen years of growth it may be necessary to train up some new young shoots to replace old ones containing many dead spurs.

In the case of a high trellis it is convenient to plant a vine at or near each post. A shoot is led up the post in the first year, and branches from it along each wire in subsequent years. The shoots from the rods on the wires are spur pruned each winter as described above.

2. *Open Work and Low Trellis*. In this case the vines are grown at yard intervals on a short leg. As soon as they are planted the stem is cut back to two strong buds and earth is heaped over them. With this type of planting, which I have not much used myself, the Guyot method of pruning works very well though spur pruning is best for vigorous varieties such as Brandt. The Guyot system consists of making two sorts of wood each year, firstly fruiting wood on which the crop is carried, and secondly renewal wood which makes the fruiting shoot for the next year. The procedure with a newly planted vine is as follows: After planting it is cut back to two or three strong buds and covered with earth. In the spring the stem is uncovered and any adventitious roots that may have formed are cut away. During the summer two long shoots are allowed to grow, and they are supported by being tied to the wirework at suitable intervals. These two shoots are pruned in the winter. One, the stronger if there is any choice, is pruned back to six buds, and the other is cut to leave two buds. The longer shoot is tied to the

bottom wire, and is designed to produce next season's fruit. The other shoot will make two strongly growing shoots during the spring and summer and may throw some flowers, which must be removed. These two shoots are trained up vertically out of the way of the horizontal fruiting stem. In the first season the fruiting shoot should only be allowed to produce one or two bunches of grapes. The following autumn or winter the vine is pruned by cutting out entirely the wood which bore fruit and cutting one of the renewal shoots to seven buds (which will make the following season's fruiting wood), and the other to two buds (which will throw the renewal wood for next season). The two-bud shoot subsequently throws two stems which are kept free of fruit and the seven-bud stem, tied horizontally to the wire, produces the fruit. This process is continued year by year and the fruiting branch is allowed to increase by one bud each year until it reaches ten, after which the new fruiting shoot is each year kept at ten buds. The stem of the vine will grow stout and gnarled, but will not increase much in height. Summer pruning consists of pinching out the growing point of the fruiting shoots a few leaves above the top wire and removing any flowers from the shoot on the short pruned stem, which is designed to be next year's fruiting wood.

Manuring. Vines need very little manuring, particularly if one is aiming at quality. The best wines are produced from poor thin soils very deficient in organic matter. In particular, one must avoid supplying too much nitrogen to a vine as this will encourage leaf growth at the expense of the fruit.

After the wine has been made, a cake of skins, pips and stalks is left in the press. This should be broken up and returned to the vines by being lightly worked into the top soil with a fork, and the same thing should be done with the wine lees. If this is undertaken every year the vines will remove very little mineral food from the soil, as the sugar, the main constituent of the juice, is made from air and water.

A little balanced chemical fertilizer can be sprinkled around the vineyard in early March at the rate of $\frac{1}{2}$ cwt. per acre of a product having a composition of about 9 per cent nitrogen, 3 per cent phosphate (P_2O_5) and 4 per cent potash (K_2O). If a vine is not making good growth double or more of the quantity should be applied. One must avoid heavy dressings of farmyard manure on young vines as it tends to make them unfruitful. If a vine makes a lot of leaf and shoots but produces no flowers, as is frequently seen in the West of England, the remedy is to stop manuring the vine and to prune the roots severely. Compost or weathered manure low in nitrogen may be used with advantage in small quantities around established plants, but it must be remembered that the vine is a deep rooting plant and we do not want to encourage surface activity: if this is done the plant may wilt in dry weather. The vine is accustomed to drawing its water requirements from deep in the soil.

Harvesting. The ripening of the fruit in the autumn can be speeded up by cutting away some of the leaves and exposing the grapes to the sun. This must not be done too soon or too drastically or the size of the crop will be reduced. It must be remembered that the leaf is manufacturing the sugar which is then transferred to the fruit. Old and fading leaves may be removed with impunity, and those young leaves which are shading the fruit from the sun should be taken off as well.

The right moment to pick wine grapes is when the sugar content is at a maximum, but this may be a point difficult to ascertain in practice. The best procedure is to allow the fruit to hang as long as it will and to pick just before the grapes either burst or start to rot. In most seasons it is advisable to make two pickings, taking the ripest fruit first and allowing the remainder to ripen further for subsequent harvesting. In other years three or more pickings may be needed, and in the exceptionally good season all the vines may be cleared at one sweep. Grapes will hang a long time on the vines and will continue to ripen on warm autumn days even after the cold or frosty nights have removed the leaves. Although most grapes will be picked at the end of September or in early October, some can be left into November, and I have seen grapes on the vine on a sheltered wall quite sound in December. The fruit should be picked when it is dry, but if this is not possible it should be left on open trays or a table to dry before it is crushed for wine. A bunch of grapes can hold a great deal of rain or dew which in a bad season can still further dilute the already deficient sugar. If necessary, after picking, the fruit can be held in tubs or barrels for a week or ten days, where it may ripen a little more, but when this is done the vessels must be well cleaned and sulphured before use. (See Chapter V for details of sulphuring.)

Most varieties of grapes must be picked with a small pair of secateurs, and they are cut off with as short a stem as possible, and never with a piece of the main stem. Cutting the ripe grapes on a sunny day is a pleasant occupation, but do remember that the secateurs are sharp; one of the most frequent accidents in French vineyards is for a picker to cut off the tip of his little finger on the left hand as he gathers the fruit. I have nearly done this myself, so I warn my readers against it. Some varieties of grapes, such as my strain of Brandt, have a fairly brittle stem and can be picked if necessary without secateurs.

It is of interest to weigh the fruit as it is picked, not only to compare one year with the next, but also in order to calculate the amount of barrel space one will need for the wine. In general, 14 lbs. of grapes will make a gallon of wine, or 6 bottles, but the pounds per gallon vary with the variety of grape and the scale of operations. On a large one the losses in working are a smaller percentage; for example, less wine is left in the press cake and less is lost when drawing it off from the lees, and in transferring from vessel to vessel.

An acre of vines in France produces about 350 gallons of wine, or 2,100 bottles; this is with extensive production, and a garden will crop at a much higher rate, easily double. Consequently, a man could grow sufficient grapes to make enough wine for a bottle a day on a sixth of an acre of land, or for a bottle a week from $3\frac{1}{2}$ rods or one-third of a standard allotment. Many people grow grapes on their houses and walls, where a calculation based on surface area of land is not of much use. When a vine has established itself on a wall it will produce grapes at a rate of about $\frac{1}{2}$ lb. per square foot. The weekly bottle will then be produced from a vine covering just under 250 square ft. of wall or about a 12 ft. length of a wall to the eaves. It will be seen that quite a modest area will produce a sizeable quantity of wine.

Diseases. There are two main diseases which may trouble the vine grower; these are the Powdery Mildew and the Downy Mildew.

The Powdery Mildew (*Oidium Tuckeri or Uncinula spiralis, Berk*). This disease shows itself, as the name indicates, as powdery patches of white mould growing on the surface of the flowers, fruit and leaves. If left alone, these patches run together until the whole immediate surface is covered with the growth. The leaves cease to grow, shrivel up and die, and the fruit splits and wastes away. The crop and growth of the vine are ruined by a bad attack of the disease, which is spread by the powdery dust containing the spores being blown about. Epidemic attacks are not unusual, and the disease is easily controlled. This is done by dusting with sulphur or by spraying with a finely divided wettable sulphur such as "Spersul". The dust or spray must be directed into the centre of bunches of grapes, and four or five treatments must be given in a bad season. In such a season the first treatment should be given before the flowers open, the second when they are in full bloom (the treatment seems to assist the set of fruit), the third two or three weeks later, and additional treatments at intervals if the disease is persisting.

Spray treatments follow similar lines, but are usually more persistent than dustings, so that not so many are needed. There is one caution to be noted. Sulphur spray will blacken lead paint where it falls, so that these sprays are not usually suitable on a house where the vine is growing near doors and windows. In these cases sulphur dusts will be found quite satisfactory.

The Downy Mildew (*Plasmopara viticola, Berl. & de Toni*). This disease is very distinct from the Powdery Mildew. All the above-ground parts of the plant can be attacked, and the first signs of it are seen on the upper sides of the leaves as pale yellowish-green patches, or "grease spots". On the underside these spots become covered with a greyish delicate mildew. They grow together and soon the whole leaf is covered; it turns yellow, then brown and dries up and falls to the ground.

The fruit may also be attacked, and even if it is not it suffers from the destruction of the leaf. This disease is prevalent in France, and all vineyards are regularly sprayed against it, but in England it is not much seen. With a more extensive planting of vines it would no doubt occur regularly.

There are two methods of overcoming this disease. One is to grow a resistant variety, and the other is to spray. The only suitable resistant variety I know is Brandt, and my own Brandts have never been attacked by this fungus; but it must always be remembered that a fungus may be able to adapt itself and attack a hitherto immune variety.

If spraying is necessary against the downy mildew a copper-containing mixture must be used. Bordeaux mixture is suitable but a little troublesome to make, or certain proprietary compounds, such as the cuprous oxide product "Perenox", can be used and are much easier to use and spray.

Ten gallons of Bordeaux mixture are made by dissolving ¾ lb. of copper sulphate in 5 gallons of water in a wooden or non-metallic vessel (a copper vessel may be used). If a wooden tub is used it must never be used subsequently for any wine-making operation as I mentioned above in connection with preserving posts. In another tub ¾ lb. of good hydrated lime is mixed with 5 gallons of water and the copper sulphate solution is poured into the suspension of the lime and stirred. The mixture is now strained into the sprayer and applied to the foliage. With the cuprous oxide compounds the correct amount of the product is tipped into water and stirred, when the spray is ready for use. The number of treatments necessary will depend on the susceptibility of the variety and the intensity of the attack. Two or three sprays are generally sufficient; the first is given when the shoots are six inches long, the second just before flowering, and the third as the fruit turns colour. In wet seasons and with a susceptible variety additional sprays will be needed, and the object should be to keep all new foliage protected by the spray.

Other fungus diseases such as Black Rot, Red Blotch and the Grey Mould (or Noble Fungus) can attack the grapes, but are very unlikely to occur in an open vineyard in England.

A virus disease is now attacking vines in France, and is known as the "Court Noué". It has not been reported in England, and if seen, the affected vines should at once be destroyed. It shows itself by an unnatural shortening of the distance between buds on the shoots, and the whole growth and appearance of the plant is stunted.

Insect Pests. The insects which damage vines to a great extent in France are not found in England. These are the grape berry caterpillars (*Cochylis* and *Eudemis*), the leaf caterpillar and the *Phylloxera*.

The English vine grower should watch for these pests and if they are seen report them to the Ministry of Agriculture as they should at once be stamped out by drastic measures. The grape berry caterpillars are very small and start their attack on the young developing bunch. The young fruits are eaten up and the caterpillars leave a mass of webbing and frass. It is to be hoped that they will not be introduced into England.

Phylloxera. This is the name of a small aphid which can live on both the roots and the leaves of the European vine *Vitis vinifera*, but only on the leaves of the American vines *V. labrusca* and *V. rupestris*. Introduced into France from America about 1870, it nearly wiped out the French vineyards, until the remedy of grafting the European varieties on to the resistant American roots was found.

Nearly all French vines are now grafted on to a *Phylloxera*-immune rootstock, but English vines are nearly all growing on their own roots, as the pest is not found in England. Consequently our vines are very susceptible to damage by a chance introduction of this insect, and it behoves all growers to keep a sharp look-out for this pest. The symptoms are:

   (i) Small galls on the leaves containing minute aphids.
   (ii) Weak and failing growth.

(iii) Following on (ii) above, an inspection of the roots will show many dead and dying roots and the presence of the aphids themselves.

Any suspected case of *Phylloxera* should immediately be reported to the Ministry of Agriculture or the local office of the National Agricultural Advisory Service.

Any vines imported from abroad will have been fumigated at the port of entry; nevertheless, it is as well to inspect the roots carefully for any swellings, galls or live insects, and to report anything suspicious to the authorities.

Soft Scale (*Lecanium persicae*). This insect is seen as a soft scale attached to the young shoots of the vine, and it is usually attended by a number of ants, who stroke the insects for a secretion they give off. The ants protect the scales from enemies and transport the young to favourable sites or "pastures". The insect rarely causes much damage to vines, but if it gets too numerous it can be destroyed by spraying in January or February with winter petroleum emulsion at 6 per cent strength.

Vine Weevil (*Otiorynchus sulcatus*). This is a large black weevil sometimes seen on the vines. The eggs are laid in the soil where the larvae on hatching live on the roots. They eventually pupate and the adult weevils emerge and attack the foliage, eating out characteristic indentations in the leaves.

Attacks of this pest are unlikely to be severe, but if they are they can be controlled by forking gamma benzene hexachloride into the soil, or by spraying the foliage with a miscible DDT fluid.

Chapter Four

WHAT WINE IS

WINE has been described by poets, chemists, traders, drinkers, customs officials and moralists in a large number of differing and sometimes contrasting ways. This chapter will describe what in fact wine is, and the theory of fermentation. When I use the word wine I mean the fermented, cleared and matured drink made from grapes alone. Wine can be made from other fruits but to describe these beverages I use a prefix as well, such as plum, gooseberry, or cowslip, while by the word wine I mean the substance as defined by French law: the product solely of the grape.

Grapes are not only the most suitable fruit because of the flavour they give the completed wine, but also on account of their having the highest sugar content of any fruit. Wines made from other crops, such as plums and figs, may be pleasant and suitable for occasional use or as appetizers, but they will never equal a wine made from grapes. Grapes will produce wine which can be drunk every day or, in exceptional years, a rare and exquisite vintage will be obtained, if the vintner is skilled and knowledgeable.

The famous vintage wines of France, Spain, Italy and some other countries have been discussed in a number of books by such experts and connoisseurs as André Simon, C. W. Berry and H. Warner Allen, but there are few works on the production of everyday wines.

To understand how wine is made we must follow the whole process of formation and ripening of the fruit and its subsequent fermentation. In the spring the vine buds open and push out shoots on which leaves form; in the axils of some of these leaves bunches of tiny five-petalled flowers are formed carrying stamens bearing pollen, and a tiny ovary bearing a stigma to receive the pollen. The flowers are self-fertile, and both wind and insects effect the transfer of pollen to the stigma. After fertilization (and in some cases even without it) the small green blob begins to swell; it splits off the ring of petals and stamens, which fall to the ground, and then if fully fertilized it grows rapidly.

In the young fruit the glucose (or the invert type of sugar) and acids begin to form together with water. As the fruit grows and ripens under the influence of heat and sun the sugar content increases and the acid is reduced. A number of other complex substances are also present, of which we may mention gums, tartrates, some oil and tannin and colouring matter in the skins, but the main products are water, sugar and organic acids, such as the tartaric and malic compounds. The exact composition of the juice varies according to the variety of grape, the soil, the climate of the region and the weather in that particular season. An average composition of the juice of French wine grapes, which amounts to about 85 per cent of the weight of the bunch, is given by Dr. Guyot as follows:

Water	78·00	parts
Fermentable sugar	20·00	,,
Free acids (tartaric and malic)	0·25	,,
Potassium bi-tartrate	1·50	,,
Mineral matter	0·20	,,
Albuminous matter, essential oils, gums	0·05	,,
	100·00	,,

In making wine, however, it is usual for the whole bunch of grapes to be used, which means that the stalks, skins and pips contribute substance to the wine. The stalks make up

(*Above*) Young shoot on a vine. The flower can be seen coming out of the top. (*Below*) Powdery mildew on fruit and leaves. The centre bunches are worst attacked and most of the berries have been destroyed.

(*Above*) Brandt vine in flower; above is a small bunch with the flowers unopened.
(*Below*) Brandt vine. Early stages of bunch, just after the petals have fallen, leaving the young berry ready to swell and grow.

about 5 per cent of the bunch and contain from 1 to 3 per cent of tannin, and from 0·2 to 0·9 per cent of acid; the skins are about 10 per cent by weight of the bunch and contain tannin, acid and (in the case of black grapes) colouring matter; the pips make up about 3 per cent of the bunch and they contain considerable amounts of tannin, that is about 10 per cent. They also contain volatile acids and an acrid resin which can give an unpleasant taste to the wine if the pips become crushed.

All these substances play an important part in making the final product. The sugar becomes alcohol, the acid and tannin contribute to the wine's taste and the interaction of all three and of other complex compounds produces certain flavours and perfumes which give wine its great appeal.

According to Nègre and Françot* on the average the

Table I.—Composition of Must

100 parts of must ready for fermentation contain in :

	Stalks	Skins	Pips	Pulp	Total
Water	3·2	6·4	1·1	63	73·7
Colouring	—	much	—	(a)	
Sugar	—	—	—	15·3	15·3
Tannin	0·12	0·12	0·25	—	0·49
Fixed acid and potassium bi-tartrate ..	0·1	0·08	—	0·6	0·78
Volatile fatty acids ..	—	—	0·03	—	0·03
Ash	0·1	0·14	0·04	0·21	0·49
Nitrogenous matter	0·06	0·14	0·13	0·06	0·39
Soluble pectins and gums	—	—	—	all	
Vegetable oil ..	—	—	0·3	—	0·3(b)

(a) Some varieties of grape have coloured flesh and hence some colouring matter in the pulp.

(b) The remaining 8·52 per cent in this column is made up of fibre and other carbohydrates.

* *Manuel Pratique de Vinification*, Flammarion, Paris 1941.

D

different parts of the bunch of grapes, stalks, skin, pips and pulp contribute the quantities of the different substances shown in Table I.

All these substances in the fruit would be of little use without the bloom on the skin of the grape. This bloom is the yeast which sets in train the whole process of vinification when the grapes are crushed.

Everyone is familiar with the behaviour of yeasts, and knows that they are used for making bread and beer, and that they convert sugar into alcohol and gas. The yeasts are minute one-celled fungi belonging to the family of *Basidiomycetes*. They reproduce by growing a bud which splits off and becomes a further independent one-celled plant and their rate of increase can be very rapid when conditions are favourable. For wine yeasts these favourable conditions are temperatures of from 43 degrees F. to 90 degrees F. and in solutions containing up to 25 per cent of sugar, traces of phosphate, calcium and organic nitrogen and plenty of air. Grape juice thus provides an ideal medium for their growth and the vintner should provide the right conditions of temperature and air supply. When conditions are not favourable the yeast plant forms itself into a case or *ascus* containing two or four spores and in this state it is able to survive under very adverse conditions. The wild yeasts which appear as a bloom on certain fruits, such as plums and grapes, have come mostly from spores in the soil, whence they have been blown around by the wind.

Unfavourable conditions for wine yeasts are too high or too low temperatures, or the presence of too much alcohol. The optimum temperatures are in the range 72 degrees F. to 86 degrees F., and the alcohol tolerance is around 14 per cent, though some strains of yeast will only be stopped working at 20 per cent of alcohol.

There are many kinds of yeasts, and they have been

classified with Latin names. *Saccharomyces cerevisiae* is the brewers' and bakers' yeast, and there are three yeasts of interest to the wine-maker which all occur in the wild or natural state on the skin of grapes. These are:

(i) the pointed or apiculate yeast, *Saccharomyces apiculatus*;

(ii) the elliptical yeast, *S. ellipsoideus*; and

(iii) Pasteur's yeast, *S. Pastorianus.*

The first yeast starts the fermentation, the second carries out the main fermentation and the third completes the process when the alcohol produced in the liquid inhibits the action of the pointed and elliptical yeasts.

Besides the three separate species of yeasts mentioned above, there are different varieties or strains of yeasts within each species, and some vintners claim that better wines result if the natural yeasts are sterilized and the fermentation is then made by the introduction of a special strain of yeast from a famous vineyard. I shall discuss this point later, but would say here that opinions are much divided as to whether the use of special yeast cultures is advantageous or not.

The yeast cells excrete an enzyme which is able to convert glucose to alcohol and carbonic acid gas. Glucose and similar sugars are those found in grapes, but yeasts are also able to convert other sugars to glucose, which is then capable of fermentation in the ordinary way. The action of the yeasts (or rather of the enzymes produced by the yeasts) is influenced by the amount of air present; if there is much air a large quantity of yeast is formed and not much alcohol, which is a result not desired by the wine-maker. If, however, most of the air is excluded from the fermenting juice, the yeasts draw their oxygen from the sugar and break up this molecule to produce alcohol, carbon dioxide, a small quantity of glycerine and other complex substances. In practice, this means that the vintner gives plenty of air at the beginning of the process in order to multiply the yeast cells rapidly, and then excludes most of the air by keeping his vessels covered in order to get a good yield of alcohol from his sugar. Yeasts are not able to go on converting sugar to alcohol indefinitely; at some point the alcohol formed reacts on the yeast, causing it to slow down its rate of growth and to form spores. This point shows a good deal of variation with different yeasts; most of them will stop at 14 per cent (by volume) of alcohol, but some strains will tolerate 19 per cent and, under laboratory conditions, up to 22 per cent of alcohol has been obtained. This means that a sweet wine must have a high alcohol content, as otherwise the wine might start fermenting in the bottle (from a stray yeast spore) and blow the corks out. Most sweet wines, such as port and Malaga, are made by adding brandy to the fermenting juice and stopping the fermentation at the point which will leave the desired amount of sweetness in the wine. They can also be made by having an excess of sugar in the juice and letting the yeast work until fermentation stops naturally, but in this case it is difficult to control the degree of sweetness in the wine, as one does not know quite at what point the yeast will stop working.

Large quantities of carbonic acid gas are produced during fermentation, and the sugar is converted approximately half into alcohol and half into gas. Monsieur Lindet gives the following table for the main primary substances produced by the fermentation of 1,000 parts of grape sugar:

Carbonic acid gas (CO_2)	466·7
Alcohol	484·6
Glycerine	32·3
Succinic acid	6·1
Organic matter	10·3
	1,000·0

The alcohol content of wine varies considerably: while it can be as low as 7 per cent, I have made natural (that is, unfortified) wine in England as high as 19 per cent, but I am fortunate in having a very tolerant yeast. If the alcohol is low the wine will not keep well, and will not travel. It will not improve with age, and there is a considerable risk that another ferment will spoil it—such as the bacteria *Mycoderma aceti*, which will turn it to vinegar. The best content of alcohol in a table wine is about 10 per cent; at this dosage the wine is not too strong to drink in reasonable quantities, and it will mature with advantage; it will travel well and is not likely to undergo any undesirable secondary fermentation.

We have seen above that 1,000 grams of sugar produce 485 grams of ethyl alcohol: consequently, we can calculate how much sugar the fruit should contain to get this 10 per cent of alcohol. First, however, we must note that alcohol is much lighter than water and that it is usual to discuss the alcohol content of wine in terms of volume rather than weight. A figure of 10 per cent alcohol by volume is the same as one of $8\frac{1}{4}$ per cent by weight. We can now make the calculation. A litre of wine containing $82\frac{1}{2}$ grams of alcohol will need $\dfrac{1,000 \times 82 \cdot 5}{485}$ or 170 grams of sugar, or 17 per cent. This means that the fermenting liquid, or "must" as it is called, should contain 1·7 lbs. of sugar per gallon. Fortunately, there is a quite simple test which almost anyone can use for the purpose of estimating the sugar content of grape juice: this is the use of a float with a graduated stem, or a hydrometer as it is called, and I describe the instrument and its use in a later chapter.

It must be remembered that wine is a complex substance but that it is convenient to think of its composition in a simple way. Thus, we have just been discussing the alcohol content in terms of ethyl alcohol. This is the main alcohol produced, but there are, according to Monsieur Ordonneau, traces of nine other different alcohols, together with twenty-five acids and fifteen ethers. It also contains, as I have mentioned before, tannin, gums, albumens, and traces of oil; sweet wines, of course, contain sugar. To keep the terms simple and to assist in the making of wine in practice, we need only to consider the sugar-alcohol content, the acidity and the tannin.

The next constituent to deal with is the acid, and it is usual to consider this in terms of either tartaric or sulphuric acid, although it is present in the form of many acids and as acid potassium tartrate (or cream of tartar) as well. Sulphuric acid is a convenient standard by which to measure acidity, though in point of fact it is not found in wine. If wine is not sufficiently acid it will be flat and dull in taste, and will not develop its "bouquet"; if it is too acid it will be too tart and griping.

Table wines have an acidity varying from 2 to 7 grams of sulphuric acid per litre. The best wines, when young, have from 4 to 6 grams per litre, which becomes reduced a little as they age. The acidity of the must is always greater than that of the resulting wine, which latter usually has only three-quarters of the former's acidity. This is due to the fact that the cream of tartar present is thrown out of solution as the sugar in the must turns to alcohol. This tartar is deposited in large amounts in the fermenting vessels as "lees" of wine. The reduction of acidity continues slowly as wine ages, and consequently a wine that is to be kept a long time must start with a good acid content. In general, white wines can afford to be rather more acid than red ones.

In making wines in England it is more usual to suffer from an excess of acidity than from a lack of it, though the latter can happen when making wine from hothouse grapes. In Chapter V, I discuss measures that can be taken to reduce acidity in making wine, and also if necessary to increase it. The estimation of total acidity is not difficult for anyone with a little laboratory experience, and I give the method in Appendix II. It is not, however, as easy as estimating the sugar content. The tongue is a good instrument for testing this in wine, though not for testing the juice. This is because in the presence of sugar the human palate tends to regard sugar as neutralizing acid, which is not the case in actual fact; hence, a must with a high acidity and high sugar content may well taste less acid than a must with less acid but less sugar as well.

The third important constituent is the class of substances known as tannins, which play an important part in making an agreeable wine. Tannins contribute to the flavour of wine, particularly in developing quality as the wine ages; they have antiseptic properties and prevent the development of diseases in wine and they also assist in clearing young wines by bringing down albuminous substances and gums. Tannin is found mostly in the skins and stalks of grapes, and consequently red wines contain more tannin than white, as the former are fermented in contact with the skins and the latter usually are not. The colour of red wine is due to similar substances, known as tannoids. These substances are precipitated under the action of oxygen, and this is why red wines stored in barrels gradually lose their colour (though not necessarily their quality) as the tannoid oxidizes and is precipitated. Even in bottle this process goes on, and red wine after fifty years in the bottle may be found to have lost nearly all its colour.

A wine can, of course, have too much tannin, in which case it tends to be bitter, or to have something of the taste on the tongue of too strong tea. In general, white wines contain from 0·1 to 0·4 gram of tannin per litre, and red from 1 to 3 grams per litre.

The estimation of tannin by chemical means is a matter of some difficulty, but fortunately it is rarely necessary. In making white wines taste is usually a sufficient guide, and the colour of the young wine is a good indicator with red ones.

As the fermentation of the must dies down, a heavy deposit falls to the bottom of the vessel. This consists of cream of tartar, yeast cells, dust and earth found on the grapes, and other unwanted matter. The wine is separated from the lees by "drawing" it, that is, by driving a tap into the barrel and running off the clear wine. This drawing may not completely clear the wine, and in order to get it limpid and sparklingly clear it must sometimes be "fined". This consists of adding some albuminous or gum-like substance, such as isinglass or white of egg, which will be deposited and carry down the remainder of the suspended particles with it. It must be remembered, though, that wine will continue to deposit as it ages, when it loses acidity as cream of tartar and some of its colouring matter.

The main constituents of wine may be summarized as follows:

(i) *Alcohols*, which come from the fermentation of the sugar, from 7 to 15 per cent by volume.

(ii) *Acids*, fixed and volatile, equal to from 2 to 7 grams per litre of sulphuric acid.

(iii) *Tannin and colouring matter*, in white wines from 0.1 gram to 0.4 gram per litre; in red from 1 to 3 grams per litre.

(iv) A number of other substances in small amounts which influence its quality to a great extent.

(v) Water, which makes up the balance of its composition.

I must now mention some of the diseases to which wine is subject. When the fermentation is completed wine is not a fixed thing: it can not only undergo changes which improve it, but if conditions are suitable and certain organisms gain access, it can also suffer additional fermentations which will ruin it, and I will mention the principal troubles of this nature. These conditions do not usually arise in the normal procedure of wine-making, and if the grower carries out the methods given in Chapter V he will not suffer from them.

The first trouble is "turning", which is the conversion of the wine to vinegar. This is brought about by the action of bacteria, known as *Mycoderma aceti*, which, in the presence of air, convert the alcohol to acetic acid. These bacteria are deliberately used in brewing vinegar from either beer or wine, but this is not the product the brewer or the vintner wants. It can be avoided by keeping vinegar away from the wine-making, so as to lessen the chances of contamination, and by keeping all the barrels or vessels full by topping up with wine from time to time (see also Chapter V) as the bacteria cannot work without air.

"Flowers" may also occur in wine; this is the growth of a felt-like fungus on the surface of the wine, and is caused by the microbe *Mycoderma vini*. In contact with air, the disease turns the alcohol of the wine to carbon dioxide gas, water and a certain amount of aldehyde. The wine becomes flat and tasteless. It can be avoided by keeping air away from the wine. Both these diseases are less likely to occur if the alcohol content is high, and if all vessels are cleaned and disinfected with sulphur fumes before use.

Chapter Five

MAKING WINE

When the grapes have been grown and picked they must be made into wine; the process falls into three parts:

A. Crushing and starting the fermentation.
B. Pressing and fermenting.
C. Clarifying and bottling.

The details of the process vary according to the quantity being made, though the general principles are always the same, and so I shall give my methods for making (I) 10 gallons of wine, requiring about 140 lbs. of grapes; and suggestions, using the same principles, for making (II) a bottle, 4 lbs. of grapes, and (III) a gallon, 16 lbs. of grapes. I deal first with red wines and then with white, and in the next chapter with making a sparkling wine.

I have already dealt with picking the grapes in a previous chapter, but repeat here that they must be as ripe and as dry as the season permits, when they are picked.

I. 10 GALLONS OF WINE: ABOUT 140 LBS. OF GRAPES

A. Crushing and starting Fermentation. Red wines, with which I shall deal first, are made by crushing the fruit and allowing skin, pulp, pips, and usually the stalks all to ferment together.

The grapes may be crushed in many ways: the traditional method is to use the feet, which has the advantage that the must becomes warmed and aerated by the action of treading. It is not unhygienic, as the formation of alcohol precipitates all foreign matter and sterilizes pathogenic bacteria and other bodies. The chief objection to it is that it stains the feet and legs a dirty brown for some weeks.

To do 140 lbs. of grapes with the feet the following apparatus will be required: two buckets of warm water, a tub, that is, a 40 or 60 gallon barrel sawn in half, and a clean sack or bath mat. For this operation it is best to wear shorts. A half-barrel (of 18 or 20 gallons capacity) with the head out, which makes a good fermenting vessel, will also be needed.

The tub and the barrel are scrubbed with hot water and set upside down on a firm floor—brick or cement is best—to drain. They must now be sulphured. An iron ladle is convenient for this purpose; it is filled with sulphur and set on a fire or gas-ring until it catches fire, and then is carried out and put under the tub. When smoke issues from underneath the ladle is removed, relit and put under the fermenting vessel. The sulphur fumes sterilize the wood and the traces of gas help control harmful bacteria in the must.

Crushing is then started; the worker washes the feet and legs in one bucket, rinses them in the next, and steps on to the sack or bath mat. About a foot's depth of grapes is put in the tub, and treading is started. The treader will be able to feel unbroken bunches with his toes (it is one of the advantages of the method), and thus ensure that all are crushed. When this batch is nicely broken, which should take about ten minutes, the operator steps out of the tub on to the mat and the must is transferred to the fermenting tub by means of an enamelled dipper. A new batch of fruit is put into the tub and the operation is repeated. The fermenting tub is best stood on a stout box or platform so that liquid can be drawn from the bottom either from a tap or by means of a siphon. I prefer to use a pair of wooden rollers for crushing the fruit as it is quicker and less messy than the feet. The apparatus, which is described in Chapter VIII, is made from old mangle rollers and can be fitted over the top of the fermenting tub. It must be washed with hot water and exposed to the fumes of burning sulphur before use. This can be done by covering it with sacking and pushing the flaming sulphur ladle beneath.

When all the fruit has been crushed, the fermenting barrel will be about three-quarters filled. It is stirred round with a stout oaken stick and a sample is taken out and tested for sugar content by means of a hydrometer. The sample may be obtained by pushing a cup into the mass and collecting juice only, as one obtains a more accurate reading if pips, skin and stalk are excluded.

The hydrometer is a glass or plastic float suitably weighted with lead shot or mercury and having a long graduated stem. It is accompanied by a long glass cylinder. The more sugar there is in the juice the heavier the liquid will be, and consequently the higher the apparatus will float. Glass hydrometers are very fragile and must be handled with care; they must be washed with warm water after use and dried on a clean cloth. There are many different hydro-meter scales, and the instruments are made to cover only a certain portion of any scale. The best system for the wine-maker is Specific Gravity or Brix, and the range needed is from 0 to 1·110 in Specific Gravity or from 0 to 20 in Brix. The Specific Gravity scale measures the relative weight of the liquid compared with water; thus, if it reads 1·05 it means that that liquid is 1·05 times the weight of water. The Brix instrument is used in sugar factories and gives a direct reading in terms of percentage of sugar by weight: thus 10 Brix means that the liquid has 10 per cent of sugar in it; but with grape must an allowance for pulp should be made and also for the fact that the Brix instrument reads the percentage by weight whereas we wish to know a weight/volume figure, so that 2½ degrees must always be subtracted from the Brix reading.

The sample is taken and strained, if necessary, through a silver tea strainer or a piece of coarse muslin into the cylinder and the hydrometer is floated in it. A note is made of the reading and from Table II the amount of sugar in the must can be found. If the gravity is 1·075, or over, the must has 1·7 lbs. of sugar per gallon, or more, and will make a wine of at least 10 per cent alcohol. If it has less sugar than this it will be necessary to add some after pressing, and the amounts needed are shown in Table II, which is based on E. Chancrin's book *Le Vin*.

Consequently, a note is made of the gravity for future reference, and the juice is either tasted or tested for acidity (see Appendix II for the chemical method of estimating acidity). If the acidity is high (over 7 grams per litre) steps will have to be taken later to reduce it.

The crushed fruit, or "must" as it has now become, is well stirred for the first day or two, and is covered over with a clean cloth. It will soon start to ferment, and the rising gas as it escapes brings a cap of skins and pips to the top of the vat. This cap must be pushed under the liquid twice a day; if not, undesirable bacteria and moulds may grow there and spoil the wine. After one or two days of active fermentation this is all that need be done to the must; too much stirring must not be given, as in the later stages of fermentation a better conversion of sugar to alcohol is obtained in the absence of air; yeast is formed at the expense of alcohol in the presence of air, which is not what the vintner desires. The liquid must occasionally be mixed, and this must be done letting in as little air as possible. One method is to push the stout oaken stirring stick into the mass and gently rotate it. This operation is done in several places, but no general stirring is given. A far better method is to draw off some liquid from the bottom and return it to the top. If a tap is fitted in the bottom of the fermenting tub this is easy; a wide clean rubber tube from the tap to a jug will prevent the access of much air. An alternative is to siphon off some liquid by means of a long glass tube joined to a clean rubber one. The glass tube is pushed into the fermenting tub until it nearly reaches the bottom and the liquid is drawn out. This is the end of the stage A, crushing and starting fermentation.

B. Pressing and Fermenting. The right moment to press the must is when sufficient colouring matter has been drawn from the skins of the grapes. It will depend on the season and variety of grape grown, and with the Brandt variety will vary from a week to three weeks, depending on the temperature. Fermentation is quicker and the colour is extracted more quickly in warm weather than in cold. The moment is judged by the colour of the must and the condition of the skins and stalks; when these are soft and pulpy no more colour will come out and the moment has come for pressing, which in general will be from ten days to a fortnight from crushing the grapes.

The apparatus needed, consisting of the press and two pins (or $4\frac{1}{2}$ gallon barrels), is prepared by scrubbing or rinsing with hot water and exposing to the fumes of burning sulphur. In the case of the press this is done by using the iron ladle mentioned above. The cage, tray and pressure plate (see below for a description of the apparatus) are piled up, covered with sacks and the ladle containing burning sulphur is pushed underneath and left there for five minutes. The barrels must be most carefully treated. During August the hoops are tightened by driving down with a blunt punch and hammer. They are then filled with clean cold water and allowed to swell. If leaking, the hoops must be further tightened. The day before pressing the barrels must be steamed, which can be done by means of a large kettle. The steam from the fast-boiling kettle is directed either directly to the barrel bung, or to it through a rubber tube fixed to the kettle spout. The barrel is best stood first on one end for ten minutes and then on the other for a further ten, and afterwards the condensed water is drained out. They are sulphured just before use by means of the following method: A small tin lid or bottle cap which will pass through the bung-hole is fixed to a 2 ft. length of wire and filled with sulphur. This is set alight by holding over a flame (a candle flame is sufficient), and when burning well it is suspended mid-way in the barrel by lightly inserting the bung against the wire. It is left to burn for five minutes, withdrawn and the bung then inserted to retain the fumes. Only the gas from the burning sulphur is wanted in the barrels, and care must be taken not to spill sulphur itself, as this will introduce a bad flavour in the wine.

The press is now set up and the calculation made from the original gravity of the must as to whether additional sugar is needed or not. When all the apparatus is ready we must decide on the strength wanted in the finished wine. Ten per cent of alcohol is about the right level, but higher or lower percentages may be used under certain conditions. If the wine is very acid it is as well to increase the alcohol content, as this will eventually reduce the acidity, and also it is as well to aim high when one is inexperienced, as a stronger wine is less likely to suffer from secondary fermentations and diseases than a weak one. The wine may be left low in alcohol if great care is taken in handling it, and if it is to be drunk young and not transported.

A general rule is for a beginner to aim at 12 per cent alcohol and for the experienced man to go for 10, unless the acidity is high, when he also should decide on 12 or more.

As explained before, the alcohol content of the wine is increased by adding sugar, and the amount needed is calculated from the gravity of the sample taken at the time of crushing. The basic figure to remember is that every 0·17 lb. of sugar per gallon in the juice is equal to a potential one per cent of alcohol in the wine. This is if the fermentation is done well; if too much air is given in the final stages more yeast and less alcohol will be formed. We assume that the fermentation will be good, and the following table shows how much sugar must be added per gallon of must, or per pin of 4½ gallons at both 10 per cent and 12 per cent levels. The first column is the specific gravity as read on the hydrometer; the second is the amount of sugar per gallon of juice; the third is the amount of alcohol by volume such sugar should make; the other columns show the amounts of sugar needed, as explained above.

Juice concentration as a substitute for sugar. It is not always possible to obtain sufficient sugar to add to the wine for the purpose of raising the alcohol content to the desired level. In this case one may concentrate extra grape juice, obtained fresh from the crusher or press, by boiling it down in an open pan.

It is best to boil off about half the volume of juice, allow it to cool, pour off from the sediment and take the gravity of the liquid. This concentrate can then be used to enrich any weak juices to the desired gravity, which is 1·075 for 10 per cent alcohol or 1·088 for 12 per cent. The calculation is made from the following formula:

$$x = Q \left\{ \frac{g_2 - g_1}{G - g_2} \right\}$$

where x = quantity of concentrated juice needed.
      Q = quantity of weak juice to be enriched.
      g_1 = specific gravity of weak juice.
      g_2 = specific gravity of desired mixture.
      G = specific gravity of concentrated juice.

Table II.—Gravity, Sugar and Potential Alcohol

Specific gravity	Equal to lbs. sugar per gall.	Potential alcohol per cent	To increase to 10% add sugar		To increase to 12% add sugar		To reduce to 12% add water per gall.
			per gall.	per pin (4½ gall.)	per gall.	per pin (4½ gall.)	
			oz.	lbs. oz.	lbs. oz.	lbs. oz.	pt. oz.
1·044	·88	5·2	13	3 11	1 3	5 6	
1·046	·93	5·5	12	3 8	1 2	5 0	
1·048	·98	5·8	12	3 7	1 1	4 13	
1·050	1·03	6·0	11	3 1	1 0	4 8	
1·052	1·08	6·3	10	2 13	15	4 5	
1·054	1·14	6·7	9	2 8	15	4 0	
1·056	1·19	7·0	8	2 4	14	3 13	
1·058	1·24	7·3	8	2 0	13	3 9	
1·060	1·30	7·6	7	1 13	12	3 5	
1·062	1·35	7·9	6	1 10	11	3 1	
1·064	1·40	8·2	5	1 6	10	2 14	
1·066	1·46	8·6	4	1 1	9	2 10	
1·068	1·51	8·9	3	13	9	2 6	
1·070	1·56	9·2	2	9	8	2 3	
1·072	1·62	9·5	1	6	7	1 14	
1·074	1·67	9·8	½	2	6	1 11	
1·075	1·70	10·0			5	1 8	
1·076	1·72	10·1			4	1 5	3
1·078	1·78	10·5			4	1 2	8
1·080	1·83	10·8			3	15	13
1·082	1·88	11·0			3	12	16
1·084	1·94	11·4			2	8	1 1
1·086	1·99	11·7			1	4	1 6
1·088	2·04	12·0					1 9

The figures in the table are calculated to the nearest ounce, which explains certain apparent anomalies. The figures are correct for gravities at a temperature of 15° Centigrade (59° Fahrenheit), but at any figure between about 10° C. (50° F.) and 20° C. (68° F.) the error introduced is too small to be of any consequence.

E

Example: Suppose we have 8 gallons of juice of a gravity of 1·0625 and thus a potential alcohol content of 8 per cent (or degrees, as it is sometimes called), and we wish to raise it to 10 degrees with some concentrated juice we have made, which last has a gravity of 1·101, being about twice the strength of the original weak juice. Using the above formula we get the following calculation:

$$x = 8\left(\frac{1\cdot075 - 1\cdot0625}{1\cdot101 - 1\cdot075}\right) = 8\left(\frac{\cdot0125}{\cdot026}\right) = 3\cdot85 \text{ galls.}$$

That is, we mix 3 galls. 7 pints of the concentrated juice with the 8 galls. of the weak and set it to ferment, when a wine of 10 degrees alcohol will result.

The addition of concentrated juice to wine must is practised to a considerable extent in France, and the juices are usually concentrated in special vacuum pans. This is an evaporating pan in which the vapour is removed continuously by a pump or other apparatus. Vacuum pans have the advantage that they use less heat and work at a lower temperature, so that all risk of getting a burnt taste into the must is avoided. It is quite possible to adapt some pressure cookers for the purpose by means of a tap-operated laboratory filter pump. The suction tube from this "pump" is connected to the safety valve of the cooker and sucks out the vapour of the juice as it is warmed. It is, of course, far easier to increase the gravity of juice by adding sugar, but concentrated juice has the advantage of adding other substances needed and also of using only products of the vine in making the wine.

The must is best transferred from the fermenting barrels to the press by means of an enamel dipper, and when this is done, wine will immediately start running from the press. The pin is placed beneath the press with a large glass funnel in the bung-hole and any sugar needed may gradually be added as the wine runs from the press. The wine which runs of its own accord from the press is known as the "free run" and is the best, and the first pin is likely to be filled in this way. It is removed to the storage rack and the next pin put beneath the press. When all the must has been transferred and no more wine runs free, the press plate is put in and pressure is gradually applied until the screw will travel down no more. This makes the second-quality wine. After the second pin has been filled the remaining runnings are collected in gallon or half-gallon jars.

Pressure is now released and the press screwed right back. A cake of skins and pips will be found at the bottom of the cage, and this is turned out into a clean tub, broken up with a clean garden trowel, returned to the press, and again squeezed. A little more wine will be obtained by this process, and it represents the third quality. After the second pressing the cake is removed, broken up and dug into the soil around the vines. This last pressing will be high in tannin so that if either of the two previous pressings, from their taste and colour, appear to be low in this factor the third quality may well be mixed with the first two runnings.

Fermentation is not yet complete, and we must still keep the wine in the warm. We now have two pins, a gallon jar and perhaps another jar of wine, all of which will start working violently again due both to the disturbance and possible addition of sugar. We must now keep the pins filled right up with wine; this allows the fermentation to throw up and out of the barrel a lot of scum, lees and unwanted matter such as stray pips and skins. The violent fermentation will gradually die down, but the two pins must still be topped up night and morning; during this period it is desirable to keep the bung-hole lightly covered, and this may conveniently be done with a vine leaf.

When the fermentation has almost stopped, the bung is

put into the barrel. The bung should have a hole of about ¼ in. diameter in it into which a peg or spile is lightly placed. All the time gas is escaping the volume of the liquid is being reduced. Consequently, the wine must be inspected from time to time by removing the bung, and the barrel topped up so that it is always full.

After the first violent fermentation has died down fermentation traps may be used instead of the above methods; these traps are glass tubes with a twist in them to hold water, and they will allow gas to escape but will not allow bacteria or dust to enter. They are very advantageous where low alcohol content wines are being made, as they prevent the access of vinegar-making bacteria; they are used by fitting them to the spile-hole in the bung. Clean water can be used in the trap, but a solution of potassium metabisulphite is better. Although these glass traps prevent the entry of harmful bacteria, some will already be present in the wine, and it is only by the exclusion of air that they can be prevented from doing harm; this is why we must keep the barrels filled. Some vintners add a little medicinal liquid paraffin to the barrels after fermentation has stopped in order that the air may be excluded.

When the fermentation has completely stopped, which is indicated by the absolute cessation of bubbling, and the weather is cold, the bungs are driven in tight with a mallet, as are also the spiles in the spile-holes, and the wine is left to settle.

The wine, to be agreeable, must be crystal clear, and three methods can be used to achieve this.

C. Clarifying and Bottling. Red wines are much easier to clear than white ones. There are three main methods, firstly cold, secondly fining, and thirdly filtering.

The wine is now in two pins and a gallon or half-gallon

jar. If it is left in an outhouse or shed it will most likely have thrown down all its deposit by the new year and the clear wine can be run off into new barrels or jars. It is desirable to keep the wine in bulk for at least a year, and all the vessels used for storage must be kept full. As there is a considerable volume of lees in each barrel, the wine running clear from each barrel will not fill a pin.

Consequently, the procedure using cold is as follows: The wine in the first and second pin and the jar is tasted and compared for quality. If there is not much difference between the two pins a new full pin may be obtained by drawing off all the clear wine from the first and making up the difference with clear wine from the second. The new pin must be steamed and sulphured before use as described on page 63. If the balance of wine in the jar does not differ greatly in taste and acidity from the second pin, it is possible to obtain another full pin by drawing the wine from the second into the cleaned (steam and sulphur) first pin and making up with clear wine from the jar. If, however, the jar differs in quality from the second pin, then it should not be used for mixing and recourse must be had to glass carboys and gallon and half-gallon jars for the purpose of storage. In the new vessels the wine will continue to throw a deposit, and this must be avoided when we come to bottling.

If the cold does not clear the wine, then recourse must be made to fining or filtering.

Fining is adding some albuminous substance such as egg white, gelatine or isinglass, or some product which will act mechanically, such as paper or sand, which slowly falls to the bottom and brings down the suspended matter with its fall and thus leaves the wine clear.

Fining has the advantage that most of the undesirable bacteria and spores which can harm the wine subsequently

are brought down with the deposit, and this tends to preserve the wine and keep it healthy. It has the disadvantage
that the albumens combine with some of the tannin and
bring that down too; this may reduce the bouquet of the
resulting wine, or render it flat-tasting due to the lack of
this substance. In the case of a wine low in tannin some
of this substance must be added before the egg, gelatine or
isinglass is used. For this purpose a small quantity of high-
grade tannin should be obtained from a chemist's shop. In
general, red wines will have sufficient tannin and will not
need any addition, but white wines must usually have some
of this substance added before fining is undertaken (see
page 75). Gelatine is one of the best substances to use for
red wines. Good quality white sheet gelatine is used at the
rate of about $\frac{1}{4}$ oz. per 10 gallons of wine. It should first be
soaked for 12 hours in a little cold water: this is then
thrown away and the gelatine is dissolved in warm water.
When dissolved it is mixed in with some wine and the whole
added to the barrels to be fined and stirred in. It will,
of course, be necessary to take out some wine before the
fining solution can be added, and the liquid taken out can
be used for mixing with the gelatine solution. About a
week later the wine should have cleared, and it is then
drawn off into a fresh steamed and sulphured barrel. If it
does not clear it is because the wine does not contain
enough tannin, and in this case a small quantity must be
added; this is very rarely necessary with red wines.

Fining can also be done by adding well-washed silver sand
to the wine at the rate of $\frac{1}{2}$ to 1 lb. per 10 gallons. It has the
disadvantage that calcium carbonate in the sand may
reduce the acidity of the wine, and traces of iron in it may
spoil the colour by giving the product a blue tinge.

Filtering is an alternative to fining, and gives very good
results, but in general it needs apparatus beyond the scope

of the amateur. Simple glass funnels and filter paper are very slow, and expose the wine for a long time to the air, where it may pick up bacteria or absorb too much oxygen. The use of an asbestos filtering-medium speeds up the process, but still exposes the wine to the air for a considerable time. In this system, a large glass funnel is stopped with a little cotton wool, a cupful of the filtering medium is mixed in with some wine and poured into the funnel. It will run cloudy at first but it will soon start coming through clear. The wine can then be filtered into a glass carboy or direct to the bottles.

It is possible to obtain laboratory apparatus which will filter wine satisfactorily using some form of pump or vacuum, but this is usually beyond the scope of most amateurs, and in the case of red wines will hardly ever be necessary.

In general, wines are best left about 12 or 14 months in bulk and then bottled. This is best done during cold weather, so that a convenient time is the November of the year following the harvest. If, however, one is short of barrels, it may be necessary to do the bottling in September just before one needs the barrels for the new crop, and no great harm will result.

Clean dark bottles are best for red wines. These must be rinsed with hot water and set in a box or rack to dry with their neck downwards. Dirty bottles must be cleaned with hot water and a bottle brush, and then by shaking a handful of tintacks in them with a little water. Lead shot can be used, but this tends to leave traces of lead in the bottle which then dissolves in the wine. Care must be taken that no tacks or shot remain in the bottle, as in bottles with indented ends they sometimes wedge between the cone and the side.

A spigot is driven into the barrels, the pen on the top

is taken out to admit air and the hole loosely plugged with cotton wool. This will filter out any undesirable bacteria in the air as it enters the barrel. A little wine is drawn and examined for colour, clarity and taste, and if this is satisfactory the filling of the bottles is started. A jug is kept below the spigot to catch any wine that spills, and the bottles are filled so that the liquid is in the neck and will leave about $\frac{1}{2}$ in. between it and the cork. It is usually necessary to adjust this level by adding or subtracting wine just before corking is undertaken. The ideal is to fill from a two-spout spigot. This has a three-way tap; bottles are held under both spouts and the tap handle turned to the right when the wine runs from the right-hand spout. When this bottle is full the handle is turned to the left and the other bottle starts to fill. With the right hand the operator removes the full bottle and replaces it with an empty one. The advantage of the two-spout spigot is that the wine flows steadily from the barrel with no checks in turning on and off and thus risking stirring up a deposit. This refinement is not necessary, however, and a simple tap spigot is quite suitable.

The bottles are now ready for corking. Wine corks can be purchased by the gross. These are put into a saucepan with a little water, covered and brought lightly to the boil for five minutes before using them. Elaborate cork-driving machines can be used and are very nice, but also expensive, and I use a simple cork driver which is common in France and sometimes found in Soho shops in London. It is a wooden cylinder with a cut-away side and a wooden piston. The cork is fitted in, the apparatus placed on the top of the bottle and the head of the piston is given a couple of sharp taps with a mallet, when the cork goes neatly home.

Bottles must be stored in a cool place and on their sides so that the corks do not become dry. It is convenient to label the wine with the year, quality and time of bottling, but this is a considerable task. It may be overcome by storing the bottles, still on their sides, in boxes and labelling these. A simple way of labelling is to use Scotch tape; the year and quality are marked on the sticky side of the tape with a red Biro pen. The writing must, of course, be mirror writing, and the band of tape should be put right round the bottle. It is, of course, easier to read these "labels" on clear bottles than on dark ones.

If the wine is particularly good or promising it is as well to wax the corks of those bottles intended for keeping some years. This can be done by melting down some candle grease in a tin and dipping the necks of the bottles in it and quickly withdrawing them. The best storage for wine is a cool even temperature; about 50° F. is the ideal, but more or less is not of much consequence provided but little variation is experienced.

The procedure I use may be summarized as follows:

1. Clean all apparatus by washing and exposing to sulphur fumes.
2. Crush grapes, estimate sugar content and calculate if any additional sugar is needed.
3. Ferment the must with considerable stirring at first, subsequently only pushing down the "cap".
4. Press, that is, separate the liquid from the solids.
5. Fill into barrels together with any sugar or concentrated juice that may be needed (see 2, above).
6. Keep barrels topped up.
7. When fermentation is finished bung down and expose to cold weather, which will clear the wine.
8. Draw off the clear wine and store for about a year.
9. Bottle the wine.

White Wine. White wine may be made from black or white grapes, and it may surprise some people to know that most champagne is made from black grapes. It is usually more difficult for the amateur to get a good-coloured clear white wine than for him to make a good red one.

In making white wine from either black or white grapes the fruit is taken straight to the press and at once crushed, when the juice will run quite "white" (that is, a greeny-yellow) at first, but with black grapes as the pressure is increased in the press it may take a pink tinge, or this pink may not arise until the cake in the press has been cut up and pressed for the second time.

Some pinkness will not matter as it will all disappear in the fermenting and clarifying processes, but when a definite red tinge appears in the juice the liquid should be run to another vessel for making into "rosy" or red wine.

Large glass carboys are very convenient in making white wines as one can see and check on the colour all the time. The carboys are filled with sulphur fumes before use as described above, and the juice from the press run in. A sample is taken as before for specific gravity and the calculation of need, or not, of additional sugar. After about two hours in the carboys a heavy greenish deposit will be found on the bottom 3 or 4 inches of the vessels, and it is as well to draw off the clearer upper liquid into new carboys, when any sugar found necessary is added. The deposits themselves may be mixed together and added to the redder wine vessels for fermentation there.

The carboys will soon start fermenting; they must be topped up as they lose liquid as described above, so that the froth is always tending to "boil over" as it were. In this way many impurities are removed from the wine. When fermentation has stopped the carboys are sealed down. They are then exposed to cold weather to clarify and the clear wine drawn off from the deposit and stored again in carboys where the wine will slowly deposit yet more tartar.

When the cold weather arrives again the wine should be bottled.

Two things may happen with these white wines: they may be a bad browny-yellow colour and they may not clear with the cold weather. To improve the colour of the wine recourse may be had to sulphite and charcoal treatment (see also section below): 2½ fluid oz. of a ten per cent solution of potassium bisulphite are mixed with 2 ozs. of good animal charcoal and a little wine and the whole stirred into 10 gallons of the wine to be treated and allowed to settle.

If the wine does not clear sufficiently by exposure to cold it should be given a little tannin and then "fined" with white of egg. 10 gallons of wine only need a very small amount of tannin; a saltspoonful is enough. It is mixed with a little wine, warmed gently to dissolve it and added to the bulk. After an interval of ten days the wine is fined with the whites of one or two eggs. The whites are beaten up to a froth with a little wine and a pinch of salt and the mixture then stirred into the bulk. The operation should be carried out during cold weather. After two weeks the wine is drawn off into fresh vessels, or it may be bottled at once. It is still likely to throw a little more deposit so that storage in bulk for about another year is really best.

If both red and white wines are being made from the same grapes a convenient procedure is to press the grapes immediately on picking to get as much white must as is required, and then to put the residue with the rest of the fruit through the crusher and treat it all as indicated above under "red wine".

The use of Bisulphite in Wine-making. Sulphur dioxide, the main gas obtained by burning sulphur, has a powerful disinfectant action on wine must and is much employed by commercial wine growers in France. This gas can be used as a solution in water, or it can be obtained by dissolving potassium bisulphite in water, and this last form is the most convenient one for the amateur or small producer. The object of using it is either to sterilize the must, that is kill all yeast and bacteria in it, and then to sow a desirable strain in it, or it is partially to sterilize the must, that is to purify it. The use of this system overcomes unwanted bacteria and leaves a more healthy wine, with a slightly higher alcohol and acid content, and sometimes slightly less coloured. A disadvantage is that the final wine may contain traces of the gas.

I find myself that I can get sufficient sulphur dioxide or SO_2 into the must by burning sulphur in the vessels, and that this is simpler than the use of potassium bisulphite solutions, but I give some notes on the use of the product as it is certainly a more accurate method of dosing the wine, though it is also a little more troublesome.

A stock solution of potassium bisulphite $(K_2S_2O_5)$ of 10 per cent strength is prepared by crushing a pound of the crystals into warm water and making up to one gallon. In practice this solution may be considered as containing 5 per cent by weight of the active gas. This stock solution is used as follows:

For washing the press and barrels: Take 1 pint of stock solution and add 9 pints of clean water.

To sterilize the must: The amount of solution needed varies very greatly. More will be wanted during hot weather than cold, and some strains of yeast require more than others. 100 grams of SO_2 per hectolitre of must will usually stop all fermentation, and this will be obtained by adding 32 fluid oz. of the stock solution to every 10 gallons of must but double the quantity may be needed in very warm weather.

When the must has been sterilized the next step is to get rid of the heavy dose of SO_2 in our sterilized must; this is done by pouring it from one vessel to another to liberate the gas. We must now start it fermenting again, which is done by preparing a "nucleus fermentation". This is a pint or so of good must in a high state of activity. This may be obtained by using a selected good strain of yeast obtained from a merchant, or by using one's own yeast from grapes known to have a good active growth of bloom on them. If a purchased yeast is used a sterile medium is prepared by boiling some juice and letting it cool to about 70° F. The yeast is added to this warm juice and the whole will soon be in active fermentation. The nucleus is then added and this whole bulk will also soon be in active fermentation and is treated in the ordinary way, as described above. To induce a rapid growth the mixture must have plenty of air stirred in in the early stages.

If one is going to use one's own yeast the method is to select some good healthy ripe bunches of grapes carrying plenty of bloom from one's best vine. They are crushed into a large jug, kept in a warm room and stirred frequently. Fermentation will soon be very vigorous; the nucleus is then added to the bulk of the must as described above.

To purify the must: From 10 to 25 grams of gas per hectolitre of must are sufficient to bring about a purification, and about the former amount can be obtained by adding $3\frac{1}{2}$ fluid oz. of stock solution to 10 gallons of must. The solution should be added as soon as the grapes are crushed. This will delay fermentation a little, but not stop it and it is very useful when making white wines as it enables the pre-liminary settling to take place before the agitation of fermentation starts.

Wine-making in a bad season. The vintages vary greatly from year to year, and we can never get a first-class wine from a poor year, but nevertheless we can do much to better our product if we recognize the problem from the first. A bad season is one with little sun and much rain, and the following troubles may be experienced unless precautions are taken against them. In the first place, mildews may attack the grapes, then they will ripen slowly, be low in sugar and high in acid. The wine resulting will be low in alcohol and may either be attacked by vinegar bacteria or by the *Mycoderma* fungus, both of which will ruin it.

Diseases are overcome by spraying or dusting as described on page 42. The other defects are overcome by assisting ripening, careful handling and the other methods given below. In the autumn much leaf is cut away to expose the fruit to any sun there may be, and several pickings of grapes are made, the ripest only being taken each time. If the grapes have to be picked wet they are laid on trays in an outhouse to drain and dry. Only glass carboys should be used for the fermentation processes, as the proceedings can be controlled more readily and smaller quantities can be dealt with.

At least half the crop should be made into white wine; this can be drunk more acid than the red, and if black grapes are concerned the half-extracted cake from the press will reinforce the colour and tannin of such red wine as is made.

A high alcohol content should be aimed at for two reasons: the alcohol/acid ratio will be brought nearer normal and the higher quantity of alcohol will also reduce acidity by bringing about a bigger deposit of tartar. One should add sufficient sugar to get at least 12 per cent alcohol, and 14 per cent would not come amiss, which will make considerable demands on the sugar ration. For example, 140 lbs. of grapes (to make about 10 gallons of wine) at a gravity of 1·056 would give 7 per cent of alcohol (see Table II, p. 65), and would need 9 lbs. of sugar to bring the wine to 12 per cent alcohol, or 12½ lbs. to bring it to 14 per cent. It is to be hoped that sugar rationing will soon be ended, though, and further the season has to be really very bad to get as low a figure as the one quoted above.

In a bad season potassium bisulphite solution at the "purifying" rates mentioned above may be used with advantage. If, however, the weather is cold at the time of using it, it may be difficult to get the fermentation started again, and in this case the must should be warmed either directly or by carrying out the operation in a warmer place. For instance, an outbuilding can be warmed with an oil stove, but take care it is a clean-burning one, as we do not want the wine to take up a taint of paraffin!

If the must or the wine is found to be too acid, there are various steps which can be taken to reduce it. These are:

(i) Building up a high alcohol content by adding sugar to the must, as described above; this is essentially a preventive method and is of no use if we find ourselves with a too-acid wine.

(ii) Mixing a too-acid batch with an insufficiently acid one, or with a high alcohol wine. This is probably the best method. The acidity of high alcohol wines gradually falls as more and more cream of tartar is deposited.

(iii) Adding carefully calculated quantities of potassium carbonate, lime or neutral potassium tartrate. I can recommend only the last substance as both lime and carbonate tend to leave peculiar flavours in the wine; potassium tartrate is, moreover, a substance perfectly natural to wine. The neutral or monotartrate of potassium combines in the wine with another molecule of tartaric acid and forms the bitartrate, or cream of tartar. This substance is insoluble in alcohol and is gradually precipitated. One gram per litre of acidity in wine expressed as sulphuric acid is neutralized by 2·3 grams of neutral potassium tartrate, and it is not advisable to try and remove more than 3 grams per litre of acidity in this way.

One gram per litre of acidity will be taken out of 10 gallons of wine by the addition of 3½ oz. of neutral potassium tartrate. This substance is thoroughly mixed into about half a gallon of the cold wine to be treated, which is then poured back into the barrels and the whole contents well stirred. The wine is then left to settle again for at least a week before it is drawn off to a fresh container.

(iv) Adding alcohol in the form of Spirits of Wine will also reduce the acidity as the alcohol combines with the acid and comes down as cream of tartar. It is a very expensive method as duty-paid spirit must be used.

We must now consider the cases of making just one bottle of wine and of making a gallon; in neither is a crusher or a wine press necessary. A certain amount of wine will be wasted as we shall not be able to get all of the liquid out of the pulp without a press, but not much will be lost by using only the "free run" as the liquid from the unpressed must is called. Average figures of yields are: 100 lbs. of grapes produce 80 lbs. (or 8 gallons) of wine; 68 lbs. will be the free run and 12 lbs. the pressings; the dry cake left will average 12 lbs. in weight. These figures are for working on a large scale.

II. TO MAKE A BOTTLE OF WINE

To start the experimental bottle of wine about 4 lbs. of well-ripened grapes are crushed in a kitchen bowl with a wooden spoon, and the must is put into a large jug, set in a warm place, stirred and covered with a cloth, and the rising cap of skins pushed down from time to time.

When the first violent fermentation has died down, in the

(*Opposite*) All the family help to pick the grapes.

(*Above*) Vine shoot before pruning.   (*Below*) The same shoot after pruning (spur system)

case of white grapes, or when the colour of the juice is a good deep one in the case of black grapes, the wine is separated from the pulp by using a kitchen strainer or colander into which a piece of clean butter muslin has been put. The must is poured in and squashed with a wooden spoon, when most of the wine will run out into a bowl set to receive it. The operation should be completed as rapidly as possible in order to reduce contact with both air and metal. A large bottle and a half-bottle should be cleaned with hot water and a little sugar put into each. If the grapes are ripe this should be about 1½ oz. for the bottle and ¾ oz. for the half-bottle. If the grapes are not fully ripe double the suggested dose of sugar should be added. The additional sugar gives a strong wine which will resist the effects of harmful bacteria so liable to gain access in handling this small quantity of liquid. As the wine is added to the bottles it is swirled around in them to dissolve the sugar. The large bottle is filled almost to the top and stood on a saucer; violent fermentation will start and much froth and impurities will be thrown out. The large bottle is kept filled by adding wine from the small one, and when fermentation has ceased the bottles are corked and set in a cold place. In two months' time the clear liquid is siphoned out of the two bottles and will make up one ordinary bottle of wine. This is immediately corked and set on its side to mature, which should be at least six months and preferably a year or longer. The lees left in the bottle can either be thrown away, or filtered for the small amount of wine they contain. Filtering is done by using a large glass funnel and a large filter paper, and is usually a slow process.

III. TO MAKE A GALLON OF WINE

In making a gallon of wine about 20 lbs. of grapes will be needed and the procedure given above is used. In general

F

kitchen apparatus can be employed, but a vessel holding about 1½ or 2 gallons will be needed for the fermentation process. An unchipped enamel jug is good, or an old-fashioned china bedroom ewer. It needs to be something with a narrow top, as a bowl exposes too much surface to undesirable bacteria in the air. The must is stirred at first and not later, and the cap pushed down as described above. Mixing can be done without letting in much air by pushing a mixing stick into the jug at a few points.

In the case of white grapes the juice is separated from the pulp as soon as fermentation is active, and in the case of red when the colour is a good deep wine one. The same procedure is used as when making a bottle only, but the vessels required are bigger. A gallon and a half-gallon jar are needed to store the wine, and these are cleaned with scalding water and exposed to the fumes of burning sulphur. A glass funnel is put in the mouth of the gallon jar with some sugar in it if the grapes were not very sweet; as a rough guide six ounces in an average season will be enough to give a wine strong enough to resist handling on the comparatively small scale of operations. If the grapes are very sweet no sugar at all will be needed. The must is poured into the funnel through a strainer, such as a kitchen colander supporting butter muslin, which dissolves any sugar to be added (which is placed in the funnel) as it runs in. When the gallon jar is full, the funnel is transferred to the half-gallon and the skins, stalks and pips are pressed with wooden spoons, or with the hands, to extract as much wine as possible. Violent fermentation will soon start again and the gallon jar, which will make the best wine, is topped up from the smaller one night and morning. When fermentation has quite stopped the gallon is firmly corked and the half-gallon is transferred to bottles, the object being to exclude air from access to the wine, and stood in the cold.

After two months the clear wine is siphoned off into clean bottles and corked at once. The lees may be filtered to obtain a little wine for immediate consumption, or may be thrown away.

Bottled Grape Juice. Unfermented grape juice is a pleasant and refreshing drink for children during the summer and is very easily prepared. Ripe grapes, either black or white, are put through the crusher and then taken straight to the press. The amount of pressure applied depends on whether we propose to make any wine or not. If no wine is to be made we should use as much pressure as possible so as to get all the juice; and the cake must be taken out, cut up, returned and pressed again, to extract the last drop. If wine is to be made as well as grape juice then the half-pressed cake can be turned into the fermenting tub, where (in the case of reds) it will deepen the colour of the vintage. In the case of black grapes the colour of the juice will be deeper where more pressure is applied but it will never be as dark as wine, as only the alcohol from fermentation dissolves out the colour from the skins.

The juice running from the press will be very cloudy, particularly that from white grapes, and it must be allowed to settle and clear. There are two ways of doing this: the first is to leave the juice in a cool place for about 3 hours and the second is to add potassium bisulphite solution to it and leave it to settle for 24 hours. The second method is much better as a far clearer juice is obtained. The untreated juice cannot be held more than 3 hours, as it will start fermenting, which will stir up the deposit again and make the liquid cloudy.

The amount of sulphite to add is ½ oz. of the 10 per cent stock solution mentioned on page 76 per gallon of juice. It is best to use glass carboys for this process as the state of the juice can then be seen all the time. The carboys are stood on a table or bench so that the clear liquid can be siphoned off easily.

This liquid is now put in a preserving pan and brought to the boil. I prefer to boil off about a quarter of the liquid and to get a more concentrated product, but this is not necessary. The boiling removes all traces of the gas. The juice is best preserved in screw-cap bottles, such as beer bottles. The bottles are warmed in the oven, the boiling juice is then poured into them by means of a funnel and a long-handled ladle; the stoppers are put in lightly and the bottles returned to the oven. Be very careful here that the stoppers are not tightened or the bottles will burst. The oven heat is increased until the bottles just come to the boil when they are taken out one by one, held with a cloth and the screw stoppers tightened. They are then set aside to cool and are removed to storage where they will keep well.

The residues of deposit in the carboys contain valuable material for wine and should be returned to any must in the fermenting vessels.

Three gallons of juice after settling and concentration will make a dozen bottles of good grape juice free from saccharine and much healthier and more pleasant than many "summer cordials" on the market.

Chapter Six

SPARKLING WINES

WHEN the small-scale vintner has made some good still wines he may care to turn his hand to the manufacture of sparkling ones. This is not particularly difficult, but needs a great deal of work, and I often wonder how the excellent French champagnes can be sold at so low a price, particularly when we consider that about 5s. a bottle is duty.

The principle of the champagne process is that the fermentation is concluded in the corked bottle, so that the carbon dioxide gas produced by the conversion of the sugar to alcohol dissolves in the wine. This builds up considerable pressure as it accumulates, and when the bottle is uncorked the pressure is released, the gas comes out of solution and the well-known champagne effect is produced.

Strong bottles and corks must be used, and the latter must be secured by wire. As the wine finishes its fermentation in the bottle this means it also deposits its lees in the bottle, and the two problems of making sparkling wine are first to get the right amount of gas in the wine—neither too little nor too much—and secondly to clear the wine.

The right pressure is 5 or 6 atmospheres, or from 75 to 90 lbs. per square inch at a temperature of 50° F. Each atmosphere requires 0·4 per cent of sugar in the must, that is, $\frac{1}{4}$ lb. of sugar per gallon should be in the must at the time of bottling. This quantity of sugar corresponds to a specific gravity of 1·0104 in the must at a temperature of 60° F.

In the Champagne the autumns are cold, and at the vintage in October, the low temperature stops fermentation at the point where just about this amount of sugar is left in the wine. It is then bottled and the rise of temperature in the spring starts fermentation again. The big champagne houses, however, use refrigeration and heaters to control temperatures and the degree of fermentation.

The next process is clearing the wine, and this is done by putting the bottles into racks which hold the bottles by their necks first at an angle of about 45° to the horizontal. Thousands and thousands of bottles are held in these racks, and each is given a twisting movement every few days. At the same time the bottles are moved towards the vertical till finally they are standing with their corks downwards. This shaking consolidates the deposit and brings it down on to the cork in a compact little button. This must now be got out of the bottle without the loss of much wine or pressure. In modern wineries it is done by moving the bottles, still cork downwards, to a refrigerator and freezing a button of ice on to the cork. The bottle is then turned cork upper-most and the cork, with its attached button of ice (and deposit), is withdrawn. As the wine is cold not much bubbling takes place; a little cold wine is added to make up for the deposit removed and a new cork is quickly put in. Thousands of bottles are treated one by one in this way, and it is the best system for the amateur and small grower. Champagne was made hundreds of years before artificial refrigeration was known, and in those days, and in fact in these by some small growers, the deposit was removed from the bottles by means of a highly skilled operation. The deposit was consolidated on to the cork as described above and the operator then held the bottle upside down, slowly loosened the cork and withdrew it just sufficiently to let the pressure squirt the deposit out. He then turned the bottle up the right way and added some wine to make up for that lost and recorked it at once. The skill necessary to control a cork being withdrawn from an upside down champagne bottle so that it does not force right out is enormous, and I have watched an old friend of mine, Monsieur Brassard of Avize, Marne, clear hundreds of bottles in this old-fashioned way without ever making a mistake.

If a sweet champagne is wanted, sugar dissolved in wine is used instead of wine at the moment of topping up the bottles just after the deposit is taken out.

The sugar wanted in the must to get the right pressure in the bottle (that is, $\frac{1}{4}$ lb. of sugar per gallon) is difficult for the amateur to estimate accurately with a hydrometer, as at this lower end of the scale inaccuracies are introduced from causes such as yeast, deposit in the must, variation of temperature and bubbles in the fermenting must adhering to the hydrometer itself as it floats in the fluid. I consequently find it best to ferment the wine right out, and then to add just sufficient sugar to get the right pressure, when this also ferments completely.

The procedure to be used consequently to get a dozen bottles of sparkling wine is as follows: We shall need a two-gallon carboy, a half-gallon jar, twelve champagne bottles and their corks in addition to the usual apparatus of press, crusher, hydrometer and miscellaneous measures. The most satisfactory corks are old champagne ones, but if these are not available stout conical corks can be used which are pushed into the bottles for about half their length; a metal disc must be put on the top of the cork to protect them from the wire, and a farthing is very suitable. Steps are now taken to produce a dry white wine of 10 per cent alcohol. If black grapes are used they are put in the press as soon as picked and sufficient juice run out to fill a two-gallon carboy and a half-gallon jar. Only light pressure must be applied as we do not wish to extract any colour from the skins. This means we shall need at least about 60 lbs. of grapes in the press. Where white grapes are used more pressure and less grapes may be used in the press, but if less than 40 lbs. of white grapes are used they must be broken in the crusher first so that we can get enough juice out of them. The juice is tested for sugar content in the usual way and any deficiency is made up by adding the necessary few ounces of sugar. The residue in the press is added to the main supply of must. The carboy is kept in a warm place and is well aerated to begin with. Fermentation will soon begin and become very active and the carboy must be kept topped up by adding must from the half-gallon jar. The object is to ferment out all the sugar as quickly as possible and this point is reached when bubbles no longer rise of their own accord though some may rise if the wine is disturbed, as there is much CO_2 gas in solution.

We now have to add our known amount of sugar to get the right pressure in the bottles. Consequently, sugar is now added at the rate of $\frac{1}{4}$ lb. per gallon of wine (or $\frac{1}{2}$ lb. for the two-gallon carboy), and fermentation is restarted by stirring, but if the deposit in the carboy is very heavy some of it may be siphoned off before restarting fermentation. When this second fermentation is active the wine is bottled, care being taken to include a little of the deposit (the yeast) but not too much. Champagne bottles should be used and filled to leave about one inch of space between the wine and the cork. The corks are inserted, the washers (or coins) put over them and the whole secured by thin galvanized or copper wire. Any system may be used, but four wires are best. The amateur is advised to take any opportunity of inspecting the wiring of a champagne bottle and to use the same process. The wiring must be tight and secure so that the pressure generated cannot move the cork at all.

The bottles are now stood neck downwards in a rack at an angle of 45 degrees, in a cool place where the wine will

slowly ferment, generate and store the gas. Four weeks
after bottling the shaking and settling process must start.
This consists of giving a rapid twist to the bottle through a
half circle, once every two or three days. At the same time
the bottles are gradually moved in the racks to a vertical
cork-downwards position. As the deposit begins to settle on
the cork the twisting of the bottles need not be so frequent,
but occasional gentle vibration of the bottles is very good.
I live near a road which carries some lorry traffic, and I
locate my rack against a wall which abuts on to this road.
The shaking seems to consolidate the deposit very well.

About fourteen months after starting the wine the bottles
must be cleared, and the freezing method is best for this
purpose. A rack must be prepared which will hold some
bottles, say six, with their necks downwards in a wooden
trough about 4 inches deep by 2 inches wide. The bottles
are carefully carried from the settling rack and put into the
freezing rack, where (if no disturbance of the deposit has
been made) a freezing mixture is packed round them. This
mixture should be two parts of crushed ice, as cold as it can
be conveniently obtained, to one part of coarse salt. Ice
from a domestic refrigerator set to maximum cold is quite
suitable, though not usually enough. A bottle is inspected
from time to time to see if the ice is forming inside. When
all the deposit is seen to be frozen to the cork, usually in
about half an hour, the bottles are taken one by one, turned
uppermost, wiped with a cloth to remove the salt from the
neck, and the cork gently worked out. Do not let it pop out.
A little white wine is added to make up the ullage, and a
fresh cork is inserted and wired in. If a sweet wine is wanted
a teaspoonful of sugar may be added at this point. Do not
let too much ice form in the bottle or the deposit will not
come away neatly with the cork, as the taper in the neck
holds the lump of ice back. In these cases most of it can be

scraped out with a small spoon-handle. The wine must be recorked quickly so as to lose as little gas as possible.

The bottles are now stored on their sides in the usual way and are ready for use almost at once, though they will considerably improve with keeping.

The clearing of sparkling wines is much facilitated by having a "coarse" yeast, that is one which aggregates and settles rapidly. Fortunately the natural yeast on my own grapes is a coarse one, but if a grower who wishes to try this has a light cloudy yeast he would be well advised to use a special culture yeast from a commercial supplier.

Chapter Seven

COUNTRY WINES

MANY good wines and cordials can be made from fruits other than grapes, and such country wines as gooseberry, rhubarb, elderberry and cowslip were a feature of village life in the days before sugar rationing. Provided they are carefully made, are not too strong in alcohol and are matured for at least a year they can be agreeable and appetizing beverages. The chief drawback to them at present is the large amount of sugar, compared with grape wine, needed in their manufacture.

The recipes for these wines are very numerous, and many of them are far too strong to be at all pleasant; in fact many contain so much sugar that this could not all ferment out and the wine must remain unpleasantly sweet.

These wines fall into two classes: (i) those in which the natural yeast is used, such as gooseberry, plum and damson, and (ii) those made from products having little or no yeast, such as cowslips, parsnips, elder flowers and so on, or where the raw materials are extracted with boiling or hot water. This, of course, kills the yeast and in these cases fermentation has to be started with an added yeast.

In my opinion these country wines, in order to be palatable, need the characteristic flavour of the raw material together with some acidity, tannin and an alcohol content of from 10 to 12 per cent. The acidity should lie between 4 and 8 grams per litre.

To get 12 per cent of alcohol in these wines we need about 2 lbs. of sugar per gallon of must, and in some cases

Table III.—Amount of fruit and sugar to make 10 gallons of must.

Fruit	Quantity of fruit lbs.	Quantity of sugar lbs.	Approx quantity of water galls.	Remarks
Apricots (fresh)	28	18	5½	Cold water.
Blackberry ..	50	16½	3½	Cold water.
Blackcurrant ..	42	17	4½	Cold water.
Cherry ..	80	12	1	Cold water.
Cowslip ..	30	20	8	Hot water. Add yeast and acid.
Damson ..	60	7	3	Cold water.
Dandelion ..	30	20	8	Hot water. Add yeast and acid.
Elderberry ..	40	18	4	Cold water.
Elderflower ..	30	20	8	Cold water. Add yeast and acid.
Gooseberry, green	32	19	8	Cold water. Add yeast.
Gooseberry, ripe	36	16½	8	Cold water.
Mulberry ..	50	16	3½	Cold water.
Parsnip ..	35	17	4½	Hot water. Add yeast and acid.
Peach ..	40	16	3	Cold water.
Pear, very ripe	80	13½	1	Cold water.
Plum, dessert ..	80	12½	1	Cold water.
Raspberry ..	50	17	3	Cold water.
Redcurrant ..	40	18½	4	Cold water. Add yeast.
Rhubarb ..	56	19	2½	Cold water. Add yeast.
Strawberry ..	50	17	3	Cold water. Add yeast.

some of the sugar will come from the fruit used. Table III shows the quantities of different fruits and sugar needed to give 10 gallons of must giving a wine (provided the fermentation is good) of 12 per cent alcohol. This means that we must get 20 lbs. of sugar into these 10 gallons of must; some comes from the fruit and the rest is added.

The quantities of sugar and water are approximate, as the sugar content of the fruit will vary with the season. The object is to make 10 gallons of must with a gravity of 1·088. Smaller quantities can be made by reducing the amounts shown in proportion.

The general procedure where cold water is used is as follows: crush the fruit in a tub by means of a wooden mallet or a baulk of wood and turn out into a suitable fermenting vessel, such as a small barrel with the head taken out. Wash the tub out with about three-quarters of the amount of water indicated in the table and pour this into the fermenting vessel, together with some yeast if this is shown in the table. Stir vigorously two or three times a day for from three to five days, and when the mass is quite pulpy separate the solids from the liquor, either by means of a jelly bag or a wine press. The must is now run into the barrels or carboys together with the quantity of sugar shown in the table. The vessels must be of such size that they can be kept full all the time, and some wine must be left over for the purposes of topping up. Do not forget that some sugar must also be added to this topping up liquid or it will turn sour. All vessels must be cleaned and exposed to sulphur fumes before use as described in Chapter V.

If a hydrometer is available the work becomes easier, and a successful process, once found, can be used again with more certainty. In this case the fruit is crushed and stirred in the fermenting tub with about three-quarters of the water as noted before. A sample is taken and the gravity estimated with the hydrometer and noted. The mixture is stirred and samples taken from time to time. The mixture is left in the tub all the time the gravity is either increasing or is steady, but as soon as it starts to drop the must is taken to the press or jelly bag. The object is to get a must containing 2 lbs. of sugar per gallon, that is, one with a gravity of 1·088. From the maximum gravity obtained when sampling and a reference to Table II we know how much sugar is being contributed by the fruit and can consequently arrive at the amount we need to add to get the standard amount of 2 lbs. per gallon.

Example: 60 lbs. of ripe damsons and 2 gallons of water mushed together showed a maximum gravity of 1·035. This is equal to a sugar content of 0·63 lb. per gallon, and means we must increase the sugar by 1·37 lbs. in every gallon of must.

From this point on the wines are treated as are those made from grapes; the vessels must be sulphured and the wines clarified by exposure to cold or by fining, and eventually bottled. It is preferable not to drink them until they are two years old.

Where hot water is used to extract the flavour, the method is to pour scalding water on the flowers, or to boil the roots with it if these are being used, leave for 24 hours, and then to run off as much juice from the brew as possible. This is transferred to the fermenting vessel together with the sugar. If a hydrometer is available the gravity is adjusted to 1·088 by adding water or sugar. A piece of toast is spread with fresh brewers' yeast, and this is floated on the surface. Some makers prefer to start the fermentation with grape yeast, and this is done by making a nucleus fermentation, as described on page 77. Ripe plums can also be used for the same purpose. Wines made from flowers usually need the addition of some tannin and acid to make them palatable. The first may very conveniently be done by adding a small pot of strong tea to 10 gallons of must. Acid may be added as tartaric acid at the rate of 11 oz. per 10 gallons of must. This will add the equivalent of 5 grams of acid (sulphuric)

per litre, and more or less may be put in according to taste.
I prefer, however, to get at least some of the acidity from
acid fruit such as unripe gooseberries, redcurrants, lemons
or raspberries. The juice from such fruits will have from
10 to 40 grams of acidity per litre of juice.

The best country wines, in my opinion, are peach, elderflower, gooseberry (unripe) and plum.

Elderflower wine has a very delicate aromatic flavour and a
very pleasant vinegar can be made from it as well; but I
would not advise any wine grower to start making vinegar.
It is asking for trouble with the wine.

Peach wine is very pleasant and is improved in my opinion
by fermenting it on the stones.

Gooseberry wine from unripe fruit is a fine, dry product
which has a steely colour about it. It is very suitable for
making into sparkling wine.

Red plum wine is very pleasant if it is made so strong with
sugar as to leave a little still unfermented, when it becomes
a nice beverage to drink sitting round the fire in the winter.
Under my conditions I need 3 lbs. of sugar per gallon of
must to get this result, of which about 1 lb. will come from
the fruit. The alcohol content is, of course, high, about 18
per cent, but my own yeast is very tolerant and reaches this
amount.

Chapter Eight

APPARATUS FOR WINE-MAKING

THE apparatus needed for wine-making on a small scale is:

1. *Containers*, such as barrels, carboys, demijohns, earthenware jars, tubs and fermenting vessels.
2. *The crusher.*
3. *The wine press.*
4. *Measures, scales and testing apparatus.*
5. *Miscellaneous: taps, corkers and sulphuring apparatus.*

I give below some notes on the preparation and care of this material.

I. CONTAINERS

Barrels. Small oak "pins" containing 4½ gallons are the most suitable barrels for the amateur vintner as they are small in size, yet have a big enough bung-hole for the introduction of a container holding burning sulphur. I also use 20 gallon and 12 gallon barrels.

The hoops of new barrels should be painted, if not already purchased so, on receipt, both inside and out. Remove one hoop at a time for painting, let it dry and return to the barrel before taking off another; this will avoid the collapse of the staves. Obviously the summer is the best time for painting hoops, and a good black bituminous paint is best. In early September the barrel hoops are driven down with a hammer and punch to tighten the staves. The barrels are then filled with clean water. Although at first they may leak, after a day the wood usually swells enough to stop this, but if leaks continue the hoops must be tightened still further. Small brads may be put in

(*Above*) The grapes being put through the crusher. (*Left*) The miscellaneous apparatus, a gallon and a two-gallon carboy. Leaning against the larger is the sulphuring apparatus: an iron ladle and the capsule on a wire for use in barrels. Leaning against the smaller carboy is a corking machine worked by leverage. The boy is using the common wooden corker. In the centre is a burette and a flask for measuring acidity. Next to this the hydrometer is seen floating in must.

(*Above*) Static tree wine press. (*Below*) Wine stored in barrels, carboys, and stone jar.

to hold the hoops down as they are tightened. Before use the barrels must be steamed and sulphured as described in Chapter V.

Used barrels are cleaned by washing out the lees with warm water, putting in a piece of chain and more water and rolling them around, when the deposit will be loosened and can be cleaned out. They may be given a final rinse with a solution of stock potassium bisulphite (10 per cent) at 1 pint to 9 pints of water.

All barrels must be provided with well-fitting bungs, and each bung should have a spile-hole drilled through it. When fermentation has slowed down the bung is driven into its hole with a mallet, and when fermentation has stopped the spile is driven into the spile-hole. To get bungs out of a barrel sharp blows with a hammer are given on the barrel staves on either side of the bung-hole, when the bung will start from its seat.

Barrels may be stored either filled with the bisulphite solution mentioned above, or dry. In this last case they must be cleaned and sulphured before being set aside. Barrels are said to be better for maturing wine than glass containers as they allow small quantities of oxygen to seep through the wood but stop the passage of bacteria.

Carboys, demijohns, etc. Glass carboys have the advantage that they are more easily cleaned and sterilized, and moreover one can see the condition of the wine more readily than with barrels. Carboys can usually be found in two, five and ten gallon sizes. There is a variety of closures: some have composition screw caps, and with these care must be taken that fermentation has quite stopped before the stopper is screwed home, as they will not stand much internal pressure and will soon burst. Wide corks may have to be fitted to others as we must be able to make a final airtight closure. Carboys can usually be obtained from chemists and may

G

easily have contained strong acids; consequently, they must be well cleaned with water and then soda solution to remove all traces of the acid. It is as well to avoid carboys that have contained oils or industrial solvents insoluble in water as they will be very difficult to clean.

Glass or stone demijohns are quite suitable containers, but they usually have narrower necks than carboys, which makes the introduction of a capsule containing burning sulphur almost impossible. In such event potassium bisulphite solution can be used for purifying the must.

The large glass bottles known as "Winchester quarts" are useful vessels for the worker on a small scale; they hold about half a gallon of liquid.

Suitable fermenting vessels are small wooden tubs, that is, half-barrels, or better still a small barrel of 12 or 20 gallons capacity with the head taken out, and the head hoop put back to hold the staves tight. These can be scrubbed clean and exposed to the fumes of burning sulphur just before use.

II. THE CRUSHER

A crusher may readily be made from two old wooden mangle rollers. These are mounted in a substantial wooden frame so that they lie horizontally side by side. It is best to arrange for the iron spindles of the rollers to project through the woodwork and to be carried in iron bearers arranged to give a gap of $\frac{1}{4}$ in. or $\frac{3}{8}$ in. between the surfaces of the rollers (see diagram). If the mangle gear-wheels are available these should be allowed to mesh together on the outside and an arrangement be made for a handle by which one roller can be turned, which will, of course, turn the other. The best system is to have one roller turning faster than the other, as in this way the grapes are more torn open, and this can usually be done by having the mangle flywheel with its small gear-wheel on one roller and letting it mesh with a

larger gear-wheel on the other roller. If, however, these
gear-wheels cannot be found the crusher will work quite well
if only one roller is turned, provided the other is free to
turn; this it will do as the grapes press against it. If rather
small grapes, such as Brandt, are to be used, the surface of
the rollers may be studded with iron boot studs. This speeds
up the passage of the grapes. The brief contact with the
iron will do no harm. The studs should be arranged in rings

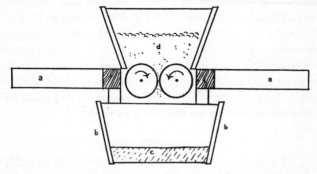

CRUSHER. **aa**: *carrying handles*. **bb**: *tub*. **c**: *must*. **d**: *grapes*

around the roller and should not be opposite each other on
their respective rollers but spaced so that a row of studs on
one roller is midway between two rows of studs on the other.
The cross bearers of the framework running parallel with
the rollers should be as close to the rollers as possible in
order to avoid grapes falling through the gap. Longitudi-
nally the framework may be prolonged to form two pairs of
carrying handles, which will facilitate the movement of the
crusher from tub to tub. Above the rollers a hopper is built
to hold the grapes and guide them to the rollers. This
hopper is best mounted on hinges so that it can be lifted
up when it is desired to clean the rollers. It is interesting
to note that an apparatus very similar to this is described in

a book by William Hughes, called *The Compleat Vineyard* and published in 1655, with a third edition in 1683. In fact this book and another—*The English Vineyard Vindicated* by John Rose (gardener to Charles II) with its charming dedication "Sir, I dedicate this *Prince of Plants* to the *Prince of Planters*"— are two very sound guides to wine-making in England.

The apparatus is washed before use and either rinsed with bisulphite solution or exposed to the fumes of burning sulphur. It is lifted on to a fermenting tub and the grapes are piled into the hopper. The handle is turned so that the rollers are turning inwards and the must will start coming through.

The crusher is not essential: the grapes can be broken by treading with the feet in a tub made from a barrel sawn in half, or even by stamping a baulk of wood on them, but the apparatus or the feet are the better methods.

III. THE WINE PRESS

A wine press is very useful to the small vintner, particularly if he is making white wine from black grapes. A wine press may be purchased, adapted from a cider press or made.

Small wine presses may be obtained in France from the "Bazar de l'Hotel de Ville", Paris, and the "Pressoirs Mabilles", S.A., Amboise, I. et L.; the latter is an establishment more than a hundred years old. Small cider presses can be obtained in Britain from Messrs. Farrow and Jackson Ltd., London, or Messrs. Stowe and Sons Ltd., Bristol. These can be adapted to wine-making by the provision of a suitable cage to replace the slats and cloths of the cider press. The smallest Mabilles press holds about $2\frac{1}{2}$ gallons of grapes and costs about £45; this is a little too small and the No. 2 model holding 14 gallons is better and, of course, costs rather more. The difficulties and cost of importing such an article may well deter the amateur vintner, and it is easier and cheaper either to adapt a cider press or to make a wine press.

Wine presses, though they vary greatly, consist of four parts—the framework, the cage, the tree and the pressure plate, and there are two main systems, hydraulic and

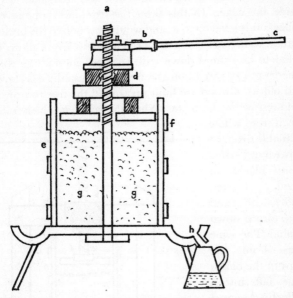

STATIC TREE PRESS. a: *tree*. b: *ratchet*. c: *lever*. d: *wooden blocks*. e: *cage*. f: *iron holding bands of cage*. g: *grapes*. h: *delivery*

mechanical. The small grower will hardly need to concern himself with the former. In the mechanical press the pressure plate is forced down on to the pulp in the cage by the turning of the central threaded tree. One type, the static tree press, consists of a base plate in the centre of which the tree is firmly fixed. The cage which holds the grapes or must surrounds the tree and consists of a circle of upright oak battens about 2 in. by 1 in. with a ⅛ in. gap between them, held together by three iron bands. The cage is usually made in two halves, so that it can be taken down to facilitate the removal of the press cake. The pressure plate is usually in two semi-circles which surround the tree and just fit inside the cage. In this press the tree does not move; a collar is threaded on to it, and winds down on to the pressure plate. An ingenious system of ratchets and levers allows this collar to be wound down with very considerable pressure. The length of thread on the tree is not usually very great, and blocks of wood are built up around the tree to transmit the pressure to the plate. When the collar has been forced down the whole available distance it is wound back, more blocks of wood inserted under it and then forced down again. The wine runs from the gaps in the oaken cage, falls into a collecting channel and is led to a delivery point.

In the moving tree type of press the tree does not pass through the must. It consists of a cage and base plate as

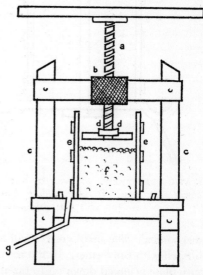

MOVING TREE PRESS. a: *tree*. b: *bearing in which tree turns*. c: *framework*. d: *thrust bearing*. e: *cage*. f: *grapes*. g: *delivery*

before, but a more elaborate oak or iron frame holds the tree in a bearing above the cage. The tree is wound down through this bearing and pushes the pressure plate down. If the tree is only short the same system of blocks may be used as mentioned above.

The former type of press is simpler, but has the disadvantage that the iron tree passes through the must; actually, contact of the must with the iron is not for long, so that little harm is done. Also the tree can be warmed and treated with paraffin wax to prevent iron contamination of the wine. The moving tree type of press is probably easier for the amateur to make.

The main item in the press is the tree; once this has been secured the rest is simple. To make a static tree press of the size illustrated, a tree consisting of a steel bar about 3 ft. 6 in. long and 2 in. in diameter will be needed. One end has a deep thread cut on it for only about the top two feet of distance, and a stout collar which screws into this thread must be provided as well. This tree must be fixed absolutely immobile to the base. Both these items are difficult, and the complicated ratchet arrangement of the manufactured press is beyond a handyman's powers. The ratchets are not, however, essential.

In the moving tree press the tree is more easily found: an old lathe bed screw of about 2 in. diameter will do, or the lifting thread of a tipping lorry may be adapted. A bearing in which this tree will run and a basal thrust bearing to carry the tree bottom and pressure plate is also needed. The tree can be replaced by a heavy lorry or car jack.

A platform and stout oak frame is built and carries the tree bearing and the tree in the top cross member (see drawing); if this top member is made of two oak baulks of timber the bearing can easily be held between them with bolts. The top of the tree must carry some arrangements for the insertion of a turning lever, usually a piece of 2 in. by 2 in. wood about 6 ft. long. The cage in both cases is made of $1\frac{1}{4}$ in. by 1 in. battens about 2 ft. long. 34 of them are held in a circle 1 ft. 9 in. in diameter by three iron bands made from $\frac{3}{8}$ in. by 2 in. strap iron forged into a circle and each drilled with 34 countersunk holes, by which the bands are held to the battens with wood screws. There is a gap of about $\frac{1}{8}$ in. between each batten, by means of which the wine escapes. It is much more convenient if the cage is made in two semi-circles with the bands overlapping and with bolt holes by which the two half-bands are joined when in use. The French presses have a system of six quick-release joining irons for this purpose, but they are difficult for the amateur to make. If the cage can be taken in half it makes the removal of the press cake much easier. A blacksmith will easily make the iron bands for the cage and will drill the holes. The exact size of the cage is not important and is conditioned to some extent by the size of the oak battens to be used for the uprights. The important thing is not to have too big or too small a gap between them. This should be from $\frac{1}{16}$ in. to $\frac{3}{16}$ in., according to the type of grape to be crushed, and $\frac{1}{8}$ in. is a very suitable average. Let us assume we want a cage of about 2 ft. diameter and have some 2 in. by 1 in. battens available. The circumference of a circle is given by the formula $d\pi$ or the diameter $\times \dfrac{22}{7}$. Thus the circumference in this case will be $\dfrac{24 \times 22}{7}$ in. or $75\frac{1}{2}$ in. The battens are 2 in. wide and with the gap are equivalent to $2\frac{1}{8}$ in. Consequently, the number of battens needed will be $75\frac{1}{2} \div 2\frac{1}{8}$ or 35 battens with $1\frac{1}{8}$ in. over. This means the last gap is $1\frac{1}{4}$ in. ($1\frac{1}{8}$ in. $+ \frac{1}{8}$ in. gap allowed), which would ruin the working of the press. We must consequently increase or decrease the number of battens by one and make the circle a little smaller or larger. It is more convenient to have an even number of battens in case we are making the cage in two halves; consequently, we increase the number to 36 and the circumference to $36 \times 2\frac{1}{8}$ or to 6 ft. $4\frac{1}{2}$ in. The diameter will now be 6 ft. $4\frac{1}{2}$ in. divided by π or 2 ft. $0\frac{5}{16}$ in. or $\frac{5}{16}$ in. more than we originally planned. The gap could, of course, be filled with a small batten cut to the exact size, but it is neater and better to have them all the same in size, shape and wood. The smith in making the bands will be more interested in the circumference than the diameter. Three strips are measured off and cut to the calculated length. One is then marked for drilling with a punch at the intervals of the batten plus $\frac{1}{8}$ in., and all three are drilled together. A saw mark is made on the sides of the three strips so that when they are mounted the bands can be kept in the same relative position by keeping the saw marks one above the other. The holes are then countersunk and the bands bent and forged with the countersinking outward, of course. The bands should be warmed and rubbed with paraffin wax before the cage is made up. Modern cage bands are made of stainless steel, but this material is expensive and beyond the powers of most smiths or amateurs to work.

If the bands are made in two halves, a great advantage, the end battens should be drilled to take $\frac{1}{4}$ in. carriage bolts at one end of each half. The bolts have their heads inside sunk flush into the batten, so that they will not stop the pressure plate going down. The other corresponding bands overlap and are drilled with $\frac{5}{16}$ in. holes to receive the carriage bolts. The bolts should be fitted with wing nuts to make assembly easier.

The wine runs from the cage on to a plywood platform, which is over the stout oak or iron base plate of the press. The pressure plate is made from oak boards cut to a width

$\frac{1}{8}$ in. smaller than the diameter of the cage. On a static tree press it is in two halves to facilitate placing and removal.

No hard and fast rules or dimensions can be laid down for wine presses. If one is to be made, the amateur will use what material he has to hand and the above hints and drawings should suffice to make a workable apparatus.

A cider press may be used for pressing wine, but it must be very well cleaned before use, particularly the cloths, to remove all flavour of cider. It is better to adapt a cider press by providing a cage on the lines described above.

IV. MEASURES, SCALES AND TESTING APPARATUS

Enamel iron measures are very suitable, and the capacity of all barrels, carboys and demijohns used should be discovered and marked on them, as this greatly facilitates calculations. Kitchen scales are suitable for weighing the grapes, but they want to be big enough to take at least 10 lbs. of fruit. A small steelyard is a useful article to use for weighing as no very great accuracy is needed.

The apparatus for testing for sugar is very important and is really the key to successful wine-making. It is a hydrometer, glass cylinder in which to float it, and the sugar table. A hydrometer reading from specific gravity 1·000 to about 1·100 is best, but hydrometers on other scales are quite suitable provided the relationship between them is understood. Hydrometers are sometimes marked on a scale of 1,000, being the gravity of pure water. This is just the specific gravity hydrometer without the decimal point; thus 1075 equals 1·075 specific gravity. Other scales likely to be met with are Twaddell, Baumé and Brix. To convert Twaddell to specific gravity we halve the reading, divide by 100 and add 1; thus 19 degrees Twaddell equals 1·095 specific gravity.

The following table gives Baumé, Twaddell, Brix and Specific Gravity equivalents:

Table IV.—Gravity, Baumé, Twaddell and Brix Scales

Specific Gravity	Degrees Baumé	Degrees Twaddell	Degrees Brix	lbs. sugar per gall. must	Per cent potential alcohol (vol.)
1·010	1·4	2·0	3·0	0	0
1·014	2·1	2·8	4·0	0·10	0·6
1·015	2·2	3·0	4·1	0·12	0·7
1·020	2·8	4·0	5·3	0·25	1·6
1·022	3·1	4·4	5·8	0·30	1·8
1·025	3·5	5·0	6·5	0·38	2·2
1·029	4·0	5·8	7·5	0·48	2·7
1·030	4·2	6·0	7·7	0·50	2·9
1·035	4·7	7·0	8·8	0·63	3·6
1·037	5·0	7·4	9·3	0·68	4·0
1·040	5·6	8·0	9·9	0·78	4·6
1·045	6·2	9·0	11·1	0·91	5·3
1·050	6·9	10·0	12·3	1·03	6·0
1·052	7·2	10·2	12·7	1·08	6·3
1·055	7·5	11·0	13·4	1·16	6·8
1·060	8·2	12·0	14·5	1·30	7·6
1·065	8·8	13·0	15·7	1·43	8·4
1·067	9·1	13·4	16·2	1·48	8·7
1·070	9·5	14·0	16·9	1·56	9·2
1·075	10·0	15·0	18·0	1·70	10·0
1·080	10·7	16·0	19·2	1·83	10·8
1·083	11·0	16·6	19·9	1·91	11·2
1·085	11·4	17·0	20·4	1·96	11·5
1·090	12·0	18·0	21·5	2·10	12·3
1·091	12·3	18·2	21·7	2·12	12·5
1·095	12·4	19·0	22·6	2·23	13·1
1·100	13·2	20·0	23·7	2·36	13·9

Methods of testing for acidity are given in Appendix II.

V. MISCELLANEOUS

Sulphuring. An iron lead smelter's ladle is useful for sulphuring tubs, crusher and press. It should hold an ounce or two of sulphur, and this is set alight by putting the ladle on a gas ring or fire. Avoid breathing the fumes as they are very choking. Barrels and carboys are sulphured by actually burning sulphur inside them, and this may be done by arranging a small capsule, such as a bottle cap or the end of a spent sporting cartridge, on the end of a piece of thin stiff wire. A little sulphur is put into it and set alight by holding the capsule in a flame (a candle is sufficient); it is then lowered half-way into the barrel or carboy and the wire held by loosely inserting the bung. Care must be taken not to spill sulphur into the vessel as only the fumes are required. Sulphur itself in the wine may give rise to H_2S gas, which is very unpleasant.

Barrel Taps. These are of wood with the tap plug turning in a cork liner. The stem of the tap is tapered and should fit loosely into the bottom bung-hole of the barrel. This normally is closed with a cork; when it is wished to draw wine from the barrel cut the cork flush with the barrel end with a saw-edged knife, place the end of a tap, turned to off, against the cork and tap it in with a hammer; the cork is driven into the barrel and the tapered tap stem quickly goes home and prevents loss of wine.

Corking Machines. The amateur vintner is most often deterred from setting up wine-making by the imagined difficulty of getting corks into his bottles, but this is really quite easy and no elaborate apparatus is needed. The secret is to soften the corks by gentle boiling in water before use. An elaborate and expensive corking machine is not necessary, but a simple apparatus found everywhere in France, and in some Soho shops in London (see picture). It consists of a turned wooden cylinder about 8 in. high and piston. The hollow lower half is tapered so that the cork is compressed as it is driven down by the piston. Part of the side in the upper half of the cylinder is cut away so that the cork can be inserted and the piston is just long enough to come flush with the bottom when fully driven home. To use the apparatus a softened cork is put into the top of the taper. The corker is held with one hand on the top of the bottle and two or three taps are given to the head of the piston with a mallet or hammer. The cork slides easily into the bottle. A rubber washer between the piston knob and the body softens the shock. A similar apparatus in brass made by "Sanbri" can also be obtained in which the cork is compressed by squeezing two sides of the cylinder together, and is then driven home by a lever.

Chapter Nine

COMMERCIAL PRODUCTION IN
BRITAIN?

THERE is no doubt that good wine can be made in Britain:
it was made in the past and it is being made today by a
growing band of enthusiastic amateurs. The home wine-
maker starts with two big advantages; firstly, he has no
prejudice to overcome, as undoubtedly he will enjoy drinking his own vintage. Secondly, he has no excise duty to
pay.

Commercial production, even on a comparatively small
scale, is another matter and it is interesting to examine this
aspect, but as there are so many unknowns in the calculation it is difficult to do so with any accuracy. Growing a
crop of grapes would be very similar to the growing of a crop
of soft fruit such as raspberries. A similar wirework system
would be erected at similar spacing, and cultivations to keep
down weeds must be on the same scale. Grapes, however,
need much less labour for picking and almost anyone can
do it. The actual wine-making demands considerable
skilled supervision and, of course, special apparatus. I have
attempted below a calculation of the cost of laying out an
acre of vines planted 6 ft. apart in the rows with 4½ ft.
between the rows. The 6 ft. planting is to economize plants,
which are very expensive at present. The plants would be
double Guyot trained and pruned: that is 4 shoots are
trained up each year which will make renewal wood and
fruiting wood along the wire both ways from the main stem
of the plant. It is a system much used in South America. If

a very vigorous growth developed, spur pruning would be adopted. The grower can, of course, raise plants from cuttings in a nursery bed, if he can obtain some of the wood, but then he must wait whilst they grow. I have taken the plants at 2s. 6d. each which is a very cheap price at present, but for large orders nurseries would, of course, make a special price, and 2s. 6d. each is a fair figure at which to put well-established plants raised by a grower himself. It is also a price at which a nurseryman might do the work if given sufficient prior notice. It is doubtful if the Treasury would forgo its excise duty of 1s. 9d. per bottle, as they do in the case of cider. " British Wines" are already made in this country from imported grape pulp and the authorities would consider home-grown grapes merely as an extension of this activity.

An acre of land is 208 ft. by 209 ft. This will give 46 rows of plants with 35 plants in each row. The rows will have stout end posts and two wires. There will be smaller posts at every 18 ft. to support the wires, and a cane to support each vine where there is no post. The wires are tightened with threaded strainers. The following are the approximate costs:

	£	s.	d.
Outlay per acre			
Posts and canes	20	0	0
6,500 yds. of wire	8	0	0
46 strainers at 2s. 6d.	5	15	0
Labour, disc land, set posts, strain wire and plant	20	0	0
	53	15	0
Plants, 1610 at 2s. 6d.	201	5	0
Cost of planting	255	0	0

Press House Equipment	£	s.	d.
Fermenting vessels	20	0	0
Crusher	30	0	0
Press	60	0	0
Barrels	40	0	0
Bottling machine	25	0	0
Storage racks and crates	20	0	0
Sundries	20	0	0
	215	0	0
Total outlay say £470		0	0

The above equipment would be capable in fact of servicing a much bigger area of vines; it would easily deal with 5 acres provided the harvest was spread a little.

The annual expenses per acre would be of the following order:

Running Expenses	£	s.	d.
Pruning and tying	15	0	0
Sulphuring and spraying	5	0	0
Harvest labour	5	0	0
Press house labour	10	0	0
3 rotary hoeings	4	10	0
Hand hoe between plants	2	10	0
Labour for bottling	7	10	0
2,100 bottles, corks and labels	20	0	0
Depreciation: $\frac{1}{10}$ of vineyard	25	10	0
$\frac{1}{4}$ of press house	54	0	0
Rent of land	5	0	0
Sundries and advertising	30	5	0
Licences	5	5	0
	189	10	0

The receipts are based on a crop of 2 tons of grapes per acre, a quite modest figure on a good fruit soil. This is equal to about 350 gallons of wine or 2,100 bottles. It is difficult to estimate the prices at which these wines could be sold. I think that discreet local advertising would lead to considerable off-the-farm sales, and provided the wine was well made, a good local reputation for it would be built up which would reduce selling costs.

Potential Receipts	£	s.	d.
1st quality 700 bottles at 5s.	175	0	0
2nd ,, 700 ,, ,, 4s.	140	0	0
3rd ,, 700 ,, ,, 3s.	105	0	0
	420	0	0
Less excise duty 2,100 at 1s. 9d.	183	15	0
	236	5	0
Less expenses	189	10	0
Profit	46	15	0

This represents about 10 per cent on an investment of £470, which is not very much in view of the risks involved in starting a new industry. Nevertheless, the figures show a profit to be possible and the expenses may well be put on the high side and the receipts on the low one. For instance the life of the vineyard is put at 10 years and it will easily last 20. The press house will serve 5 acres so its depreciation should be spread over this area of vines; with those reductions the profit is more encouraging.

It is, however, the Customs and Excise regulations that will cause the most inconvenience to the would-be commercial wine grower; though I think he would get every help and consideration from the officials concerned, he must take out the necessary licences and pay the requisite duty. As I mentioned above, the Treasury will regard farm production merely as an extension of the considerable "British Wine" industry already established, which makes wines

H

from imported juice concentrates. This is a bigger industry than may be imagined: in 1950 the output was 3·8 million gallons and paid £2,814,500 in duty. If farmers were allowed to sell duty-free wine it would be difficult not to permit the "British Wine" makers similar privileges, and the Treasury would be loth to forgo this large source of revenue.

Consequently to keep within the law the would-be vintner must take out a licence to manufacture "Sweets". (For some inexplicable reason the Customs and Excise use this term to refer to wine-making.) This costs £5 5s. od. annually.

It allows the maker to sell wines wholesale, provided the excise duty is paid on them. By "wholesale" is meant a sale of 2 gallons or more to any one purchaser, or of a dozen quart bottles or more. It does not allow retailing of wines; for this a retailer's "off" licence must be obtained from the justices, which may be a matter of some difficulty.

In order to ensure the correct payment of the excise duty certain conditions in regard to the winery must be fulfilled. A plan of the buildings must be submitted to the Excise Officer, with the description of the use of each vessel and all apparatus on the premises.

The rooms, vessels and apparatus must be labelled with their purpose, and wine on which duty has been paid must be kept segregated from wine which has not completed its excise.

A record must be kept of all entries and withdrawals of wine and of materials used, and this must always be available for inspection by the excise officers.

Scales, weights, ladders and lights must always be available for the officer, who is entitled to enter the premises at any time and to take samples and make an inspection of vessels and of the books.

The present duties are at the rate of 10s. 6d. per gallon on wines of 26 degrees of proof spirit, and £1 10s. 6d. per gallon on fortified wines of over this strength.

Proof spirit is alcohol which contains 57 per cent by volume of pure alcohol. It arose from a rough and ready test of older times for assessing the rate of duty on brandy. A small heap of gunpowder was put on a metal plate and wetted with the spirit. This spirit was then lit and if the brandy was strong the flame would light the gunpowder, which would then flare up. If it was weak, in fact below 57 per cent by volume, it would contain enough water to wet the powder and prevent it from burning. Analysis has now, of course, replaced this primitive "proof" of spirit.

Wine of "27 degrees of proof" contains 27 per cent of 57 per cent alcohol or 15·4 per cent by volume of alcohol. Over this figure it must pay at the higher rate.

The duty must be paid every Monday on all wine sent out the previous week, but arrangements can be made to pay monthly if a bond is given to the Excise Office.

The regulations allow duty-free samples to be sent out provided they are in 8 oz. bottles or smaller.

The vintner must take stock twice a year, on 1st October and 1st April, and make an annual financial statement. The Excise Officer will also supply an Entry Book and a record of all entries and withdrawals must be kept in this volume.

There are a number of other small points which I have not covered but these omissions are not of great importance. Though the regulations sound complex I think in practice the vintner would find the proceeding relatively simple provided he can adapt his premises well and learns to co-operate readily with the excise officers.

The vintner may sometimes need sugar for the purpose of raising the gravity of his must: the quantity needed is not likely to be more than from ½ to 1 cwt. per acre unless the season is very bad, and an application for sugar for manu-

facturing purposes made to the Ministry of Food is likely
to be received sympathetically.

Wine is a pleasant thing, and wine one has made oneself
is yet pleasanter. I hope I have shown in this book that it
can readily be made in England if a little care and attention
is given to the matter. It used to be made—in Appendix I
I give some notes on old English vineyards and a bibliography of books on the subject—and it still is made by
quite a large number of gardeners. My own wines from
good years, such as 1945 and 1947, have been commented
upon very favourably by connoisseurs and have won com-
mendation in a B.B.C. programme.

Our climate does not inhibit the growth and cropping of
the early vine varieties; it is very similar to the climate of
the Champagne, Moselle and Rhine vine lands, and what
it may sometimes lack in summer heat is largely made up
by the longer duration of the day.

I hope at least gardeners will be encouraged to plant
vines; so many houses have their south walls bare and these
are just the places for vines. Even if the lower 10 feet of a
house wall is used for peaches or pears, the upper part can
be clad with a vine carried up on a long stem, and allowed
to branch out there. The amateur should plant two or three
different varieties as his particular soil may suit one better
than another. I also hope that some commercial fruit
growers will try an acre or so of vines. Even if the wine is
not sold it would be enjoyed by his family and make a very
welcome addition to the harvest supper. He can make
wine on his farm for about the same price, or even less,
than the figure he will have to pay for beer.

The English vintner need be no Mr. Mountchesney, who
rather liked bad wine, but can make, drink and enjoy his
wine with a merry heart.

Appendix No. I

*Bibliography and Notes on Vines in England
from Roman Times to* 1900

In this appendix the date (A.D.) is first given, then the authority and primary reference. Any secondary reference then appears in brackets, followed by a note on the matter or the name of the book. The numbers, such as "BM. 7076", refer to the British Museum bench marks for books. In this list the name of a book is only given once, all subsequent references are to the author only.

A.D. 280: PROBUS. Volpiscus. (J. L. Denham, *The Vine and its Fruit*, Longmans, 1875, *also* E. Hyams, *The Grape Vine in England*, Bodley Head, 1949.) Repealed the edict of Domitian prohibiting planting of vines in Britain.

"Anciently": DR. PLOTT. (André Simon, *English Wines and Cordials*, Gramol, London, 1946.) Wine made all over the country.

731: VENERABLE BEDE, THE. *Historia Ecclesiastica*. (C. W. Berry, *Viniana*, Constable, 2nd edn., 1934.) Vines found in a few places.

Saxon Times: STRUTT, J. *Doend Angel, or Manner of the inhabitants of England*, BM. 7917-dd-15. 1775. In the *Doend Angel* it is said that the Saxons called October the "Wyn Monat".

"Ancient Times": *Ely Church Archives*. (Quoted in W. Speechly's *Treatise on the Cult. of the Vine*, London, 1790.) Salaries of the vine dressers given.

871–901: *Laws of Alfred*. (A. Simon.) Mention of vineyards.

957–975: *Laws of Edgar*. (A. Simon.) Gift of a vineyard at Wyat.

1080: *Domesday Book*. (Sir H. Ellis, *A General Introduction to the Domesday Book*, London, 1833, BM. 2082 B.) Thirty-eight references to vineyards. Six arpents of vines at Sevin, Essex. Twelve arpents at Risham, Berks, Ramsey, E. Anglia, Hanton, Winchester, etc.

"After the Conquest": CAMDEN. *Brittania*, 2nd ed., 1722. Normans drank their own home-made wine; no trade in it. Vineyards at Worcester, Gloucester, Tewkesbury, Ledbury, Westminster, Chenstone, Middlesex, Ware, and other places.

11th century: An illuminated 11th-century Pentateuch, B.M.Ms. Claudius B. IV. fol. 17 written in Latin and Saxon, shows a vineyard being tended and grapes being pressed. See the plate opposite page 32 of this book.

1114–1134: HENRY I. (A. Simon.) Henry I had vine dressers on his staff.

*c.*1120: WILLIAM OF MALMESBURY. *De Regibus Anglorum*. (A. Simon.) Records vineyards in Gloucester. Domain of Thorney, Ely, so fully cultivated with apples and vines that it was like an earthly Paradise.

1140: SHERIFFS OF NORTHAMPTON AND LEICESTER. (A. Simon.) Money allowed for livery of the King's vine dresser. Record of two vineyards at Maldon.

1143: STEPHEN. (A. Simon.) Acts of this reign call for restoration of a vineyard from Holy Trinity Priory, London, to original owner.

1150: EADWIN. *Canterbury Great Psalter*, 1150: facsimile Lund Humphries, 1935. (E. Hyams.) A sketch of vine dressing.

1155 onwards: *Windsor Pipe Rolls*. (Lambarde, *Dict. Angliae Topograficum et Historicum*, 1573.) Charges of the grape harvest appear regularly.

1162, 1165, 1174, 1175, 1189, Richard I, Henry III,
Edward II, Richard II: *Exchequer Rolls*. (A. Simon.)
Many mentions of the royal vineyards. Windsor, Purley,
Stoke, Cislet, Hereford, Huntingdon, Tenham.

1175: NECKHAM, ALEXANDER: *De Naturis Rerum*. (Hyams
and Sir Stephen Gaselee's *Natural Science in England at
the end of the 12th Century*, London, 1936.) Describes the
harvest of grapes and how the pickers burst into song
when they had finished.

1208-9: *Pipe Roll*, Winchester. (A. Simon.) Bishop of
Winchester sold wines

13th century: *Spalding Priory Register*. (A. Simon.) John
the Almoner planted a vineyard.

1276: *Exchequer Rolls*. (A. Simon.) Cantilupe, Bishop of
Hereford, planted a vineyard at Ledbury and made
seven casks in 1289.

13th and 14th centuries: *Archives of Court of Pleas of the
Forest and Honours, Windsor*. Cited in J. Stow's *Flores
Historearum*, 1600. (A. Simon.) Yearly account of the
charges of planting vines.

1307–1327 (Edward II): LAMBARDE, WILLIAM, *Dict.
Angliae Topograficum et Historicum*, 1573. (A. Simon.) The
Bishop of Rochester made wine and gave some to the
King. Many vines near Santlac, Battle Abbey.

1377–1399 (Richard II): *Records, Honour Court Windsor Castle*.
Cited in *Howe's Annals*, p. 143, 1631. (*Archaeology*, Vol. I,
p. 319, Vol. IV, p. 67.) Yearly account of vine planting.

1483: *Harlington MS*. No. 438, fol. 135. (A. Simon.) Richard
III gave John Piers 6d. per day for life as master of the
vineyard.

1572: MASCALL, LEONARD. *A Booke of the Arte and Manner
of how to plant and graffe all sortes of trees*, London, 1572.
BM. 453, a. 2. Gives directions for growing grapes and
making wine.

1577: HOLINSHED, R. *Chronicles of Holinshed*. London, 1577. BM. 598, h.34. (Denham, 1875.) Maintains that lack of English wine was not due to soil but negligence.

1608: KNIGHT, H. P. *Flores Paradisae*, London, 1608. BM. 969, a. 41. Describes planting vineyards and making wine.

1640: PARKINSON, JOHN. *Theatrum Botanicum*, London. T. Cotes, BM. 450, i. 7. (E. Hyams.) A chapter on vines (No. IV).

1650: SOMNER, W. *The Antiquities of Canterbury*, c. 1650. (A. Simon.) Numerous vineyards in Kent, St. Augustine's Abbey, Colton, St. Martin's, Chertham, Brook, Hollingbury.

1655: EVELYN, JOHN. *Evelyn's Diary*, 26 September 1655. ". . . to see Col. Blount's subterranean warren and drank the wine of his vineyard, which was good for little."

1655: HUGHES, WILLIAM. *The Compleat Vineyard*, 1st ed., 1665(?), 3rd ed. 1683. London, Will. Crook, BM. 7076, a. 25 (ref. in G. E. Fussell's bibliography). Discusses foreign methods of making wine.

1666: ROSE, JOHN. *The English Vineyard Vindicated*. Preface by 'Philocepos' (John Evelyn), London, 1666, BM. 448, a. 17. (G. F. Fussell.) Rose was gardener to the King; he gives clear instructions for growing vines and offers plants.

1669: DIGBY, SIR KENELM. *The Closet of the Eminently Learned Sir Kenelm Digby*, London, 1669. BM. 1037.3. 10. (G. F. Fussell.) Gives recipes for country wines, and advocates the use of a primitive hydrometer, that is, to add honey till a fresh egg floats "to the depth of two-pence".

1670: HANMER, THOMAS. *Garden Book*, London, 1670. Re-issued 1933, ed. Eleanor S. Rohde. (E. Hyams.)

Gives advice on growing vines, particularly on pruning.
Refers to Col. Blount, whose wine Evelyn did not
like.

1676: WORLIDGE, JOHN. *Vinetum Brittanicum*, 1676. BM.
7078.666.1. (Wine Trade Club Library.) Though dealing
with cider he also describes how to plant a vineyard.

1677: BEALE, JOHN. *Nurseries, Orchards, Profitable Gardens and
Vineyards encouraged*, London, Henry Braine, 1677. BM.
966, b. 35. (G. E. Fussell.) Refers to Rose and advocates
reinforcement with sugar.

1694: Y-WORTH, W. *The Britannia Magazine, or a New
Arte of Making Twenty Sortes of English Wine*, London,
2nd ed. 1694. W. Olney for T. Salisbury. BM 969 a. 45.
Gives rather vague directions for making wine.

End of 17th century: SKIPP, GEORGE. (A. Simon.) Made
red and white wine at Upper Hall, Ledbury.

1717: COLLINS, SAMUEL. *Paradise Retrieved—Method of
Managing and Improving Fruit Trees*, J. Collins, R. Burleigh,
London 1717. BM. 452.6.26. Gives accounts of vine-
yards, with a sketch of how to train vines on a wall.

1722: FAIRCHILD, THOMAS. *The City Gardener*, T. Woodward,
J. Peele, London, 1722. BM. 452, C. 26. (E. Hyams.)
An account of vines in Leicester Fields and many tavern
yards.

1727: J. S. *The Vineyard, a treatise . . . being the observations of
a gentleman in his travels*, London, 1727. BM. 966, b. 10.
(G. E. Fussell.) A treatise on foreign methods of making
wine, with every system of growing in England.

1733: BROWNE, D. *The Vineyard . . . a method of planting
vines in England*, 9th ed., 1733. (S. W. Cheveley's library.)
An advertisement for this book is at the back of Browne's
book on hops, 1733.

1733: GRAHAM, WILLIAM. *The Arte of Making Wine from
Fruits, Flowers and Herbs*, 8th ed. 1733, London. W.

Nicholl. (Wine Trade Club Library.) Suggests the addition of sugar to muscat grapes to make good wine.

1739: MILLER, P. *The Gardener's Dictionary*, London, Rivington, 1739. Article on vines describes how to make English wine, and advises against imitating foreign wines. The author was a famous introducer of plants and gardener to the Apothecaries.

1775: BARRY, SIR EDWARD. *Observations, Historical, Critical and Medical on the Wine of the Ancients*, London, T. Cadell, 1775. BM. 449 i. 9. (*Country Life*, Vol. I, p. 239, 1897.) Refers to successful wine made by Hon. Chas. Hamilton from his grapes at Pain's Hill, Surrey, and describes methods.

1786: LE BROCQ, PETER. *A Description with Notes of Certain Methods of Planting, Training and Management of Fruit Trees, Vines, etc.*, P. Le Brocq, London, 1786. BM. B. 540–(3). (G. L. Fussell.) Succeeded in getting a letters patent for his method of training fruit and vines, and threatened with prosecution anyone who infringed it without paying the fee, thus discouraging planting.

1786: VISPRÉ, F. X. *A Dissertation on the Growth of Wine in England*, R. Crutwell, Bath, 1786. BM. B.675 (3). (G. L. Fussell.) Any part that will ripen wheat in August will ripen grapes in October. Even in a wet summer (1784) at Chelsea he ripened grapes. He defies Le Brocq and his informers and patent!

1787: VISPRÉ, F. X. *Le Vin du Pays*, T. Spilbury, Londres, 1787. BM. 8226. dd. 14 (1–9). A long account of wine growing in Britain and its good future possibilities. Arguments with Barrington and Le Brocq.

1790: SPEECHLEY, W. *A Treatise on the Culture of the Vine*, London, 1790. BM. 433, f.21. 3rd ed. 1821. BM. 7078, df. 19. (G. E. Fussell.) A plate shows a vine said to be 150 years old on a house at Northallerton. Speechley was gardener to the 3rd Duke of Portland at Welbeck Abbey. His wines sold retail at 7s. 6d. to 10s. a bottle, a high price.

1802: SAVAGE & MEYLER. *Bath and Five Miles Around*, Bath 1802. (Bath Public Library). This map shows a vineyard at Clevedon. Terraces can still be seen, and the place is called "Vineyard Farm".

1803: FORSYTH, WILLIAM. *A Treatise on the Culture of Fruit Trees*, Longman-Rees, London, 1803. (Wine Trade Club Library.) Advises on how to grow vines on walls and recommends serpentine system of training.

1808 et ante: DAVIES, J. *The Innkeepers and Butler's Guide, or a Directory to British Wines*, G. Watson, Leeds, 6th ed. 1808. (Wine Trade Club Library.) Gives recipes for making imitation foreign wines.

1819: REES, A. *The Cyclopedia, or Universal Dictionary*, Longmans, London, 1819. (Wine Trade Club Library.) Maintains vines should grow well in Britain; many cottages in Sussex grow them. He gives instructions, and quotes Dr. Maculloch and Pain's Hill.

1833: REDDING, C. *History and Description of Modern Wines*, Whittaker, Trencher and Arnott, 1833. (Wine Trade Club Library.) Wine might easily be grown in England, but there are more profitable crops available.

1835: ROBERTS, W. H. *The British Winemaker and Domestic Brewer*, Edinburgh, 1st ed. 1835, 4th 1847, 5th 1849. BM. 1037, b. 27, 46, 34. He gives detailed descriptions for making fruit and grape wines, and full instructions for the use of the hydrometer.

1864: SHEEN, J. R. *Wines and other fermented Liquors, from the earliest times to the present day*, London, 1864. (Wine Trade Club Library.) Somewhat copies Barry's book of previous century; discusses British wines.

1875: DENHAM, J. L. *The Vine and its Fruits*, Longmans, London, 1875. (Wine Trade Club Library.) Gives a long account of the growth of vines in Britain and of methods of making wine.

1875–1915 (?): BUTE, MARQUIS OF, & PETTIGREW, A. in *The Fruit Garden*, by George Bunyard, *Country Life*, London, 1904. (E. Hyams.) The successful vineyard at Castle Coch was started in 1875 and continued at Swanbridge. In 1881 all wines sold wholesale at 5s. per bottle and retail at over 9s. two years later.

1890: ELLACOMBE, REV. CANON, H. N. *Vineyards of Somerset and Gloucester*, Bath Natural History and Antiquarian Club. Vol. III, p. 34. 15 January 1890. Discusses the vineyards in the west in the past and mentions one lost at Tortwell in 1803 because of a dispute with the rector.

Appendix No. II

Determination of Acidity in Wine or Must

The total acidity is estimated by titration against potassium hydroxide solution equivalent to 10 grams per litre of sulphuric acid.

The following materials will be needed:

1. A burette graduated in cubic centimetres and tenths and stand.
2. A 10 cc. pipette.
3. Litmus paper, blue.
4. A 50 cc. conical flask.
5. A small glass funnel.
6. A solution of potassium hydroxide equivalent to 10 grams per litre of sulphuric acid; that is, it should contain 11·43 grams of pure potassium hydroxide per litre. Such a solution is best obtained from a chemical supply house, industrial laboratory or technical college. It must be kept in a glass-stoppered bottle.

The procedure is as follows: rinse the burette out with a little of the solution and throw this away. Set the burette in its stand, put the funnel into the top and fill to just over the zero mark with the solution. Take the funnel out and open the tap till the lower meniscus of the liquid just cuts the zero line. Stir the must or wine to be tested and take out a sample. Suck up a pipette full and then throw this away, then fill the pipette again to above the mark on the stem and hold the liquid there by placing the finger over the end. The finger is then lifted a little to allow the liquid slowly to run out, and this is stopped when the mark is reached. The pipette will now have exactly 10 cubic centimetres in it and the contents are run into the small flask. Add a piece of litmus paper, which will turn red, then put under the burette, and by means of the tap gradually add the hydroxide solution, shaking the flask around from time to time, until the paper just turns blue again. The number of ccs. used will be the acid content of the sample in grams of sulphuric acid per litre. If the result is wanted in terms of tartaric acid the figure should be multiplied by 1·53. It is best to make three determinations and to take their average. It is not necessary to fill the burette to the zero mark each time, provided the beginning and ending points are noted and the difference taken.

Example:

	Reading at start	Reading at end	Grams per litre of acidity
1st	0	4·6	4·6
2nd	4·6	9·4	4·8
3rd	9·4	13·8	4·4
			13·8
		Average:	4·6

Appendix No. III

Determination of Alcohol in Wine

The best method of estimating the percentage of alcohol in wine is to take a certain quantity, then distil off half this amount and take the specific gravity of the distillate by means of floating a special hydrometer in it. This gives a direct reading of the alcohol contained in the liquid, and half this figure will be the concentration of alcohol in the original wine, as the distillate contains all the alcohol of the wine in half the volume as distillate.

The size of the apparatus is determined by the quantity of fluid needed to float the hydrometer. If this is, say, 100 ccs. the following apparatus will be needed:

1. 500 cc. distillation flask.
2. Condenser and connections to fit to flask.
3. Measuring cylinder, 100 ccs.
4. Hydrometer reading from 0 to about 35 degrees of alcohol.
5. Thermometer.
6. Gas burner or electric ring.

Proceed in the following way: set up the apparatus and turn on the condensing water; pour into the flask 200 ccs. of wine, add a small piece of broken glass and a little solid potassium hydroxide. If the wine is new add a little lard or butter as this will stop frothing. Wash out the measuring cylinder, dry it and set it under the delivery of the condenser. Turn on the heat and distil off exactly 100 ccs. of liquid. Take the temperature of this, and if it is about 15° C. float the alcoholmeter (which must be very clean) in it. Half the reading on this where the stem sticks out of the fluid will be the percentage of alcohol by volume in the wine. If the temperature is above or below 15° C. the reading will be more or less than the true one, but errors of less than 5 per cent will be caused by readings made between temperatures of 12° and 18°.

A specific gravity hydrometer reading from 1 to 0·9590 (that is, over a different range than that used for the sugar in the must) can be used and reference made to a table of alcohol gravities in a chemist's handbook, but the direct reading alcoholmeter is much more satisfactory and rapid.

It should be noted that it is illegal to use a chemist's still in Britain unless a licence has been taken out, price 10s. per annum.